GREEKA

EAGLE OF THE HEBRIDES

Greeka
Eagle of the Hebrides

BY

JOSEPH E. CHIPPERFIELD

Drawings by
Larry Toschik

LONGMANS, GREEN AND CO.

NEW YORK · LONDON · TORONTO

1954

LONGMANS, GREEN AND CO., INC.
55 FIFTH AVENUE, NEW YORK 3

LONGMANS, GREEN AND CO., LTD.
6 & 7 CLIFFORD STREET, LONDON W 1

LONGMANS, GREEN AND CO.
215 VICTORIA STREET, TORONTO 1

GREEKA

PUBLISHED SIMULTANEOUSLY IN THE DOMINION OF CANADA BY
LONGMANS, GREEN AND CO., TORONTO

FIRST EDITION

LIBRARY OF CONGRESS CATALOG CARD NUMBER 54-6666

Printed in the United States of America

To
"ABBY" and BILL
my companions in the Hebrides
when searching for the Golden
Eagle
and to the MacLennans of Carbost
and Doctor Colin MacDonald, all
of whom did much to aid my success,
making my stay on the Isle of Skye
such a memorable occasion

Thrice the life of a dog the life of a horse,
Thrice the life of a horse the life of a man,
Thrice the life of a man the life of a stag,
Thrice the life of a stag the life of an EAGLE,
Thrice the life of an eagle the life of an oak tree.

OLD HIGHLAND ADAGE

CONTENTS

xi

OTHER BOOKS BY

MR. CHIPPERFIELD

Storm of Dancerwood

Windruff of Links Tor

Beyond the Timberland Trail

GREEKA

EAGLE OF THE HEBRIDES

CHAPTER ONE

THE EYRIE ON ROINEVAL

NIGHT CAME SUDDENLY TO BEALACH MOR — AN EXPANSE
of bog and mountain north of Loch Harport on the island
of Skye. There was little or no twilight that evening. The
last of the April day had, a good hour since, glowed with
angry splendor behind the vast tableland of the Trotternish
Mountains. For a few minutes, the fantastic sunset found
reflection in the tarns and lochs. It brought into stark relief
the Storr Rocks that marked the northern limits of the eagles'
glen, while in the southeast, the crags of the Black Cuillins
appeared queerly softened in the afterglow.

The sunset, however, was of short duration. The light
went quickly from the sky, and darkness invaded the moor
almost at once.

There were no stars and no moon. The sheep stood in
melancholy isolation in the hollows. Nothing moved. Even
the burn that flowed down to the falls above the Dunvegan
road seemed to have lost a little of its boisterous mirth and
certainly all of its spumy chatter.

Towering over Bealach Mor, the volcanic crags of Roineval appeared ominous in outline — a sprawling ridge that

contained innumerable gullys and ledges that were the homes of many creatures of the wild.

On one of the ledges which, in daylight, looked out over the entire glen, was Groonah, the golden eagle. She rested with pinions outstretched, nestling her young close against her breast feathers as the night came riding swiftly up the slope.

Like Roineval, which afforded her shelter, she was omnipotent. The fierceness of her eye only softened when she felt a quiet movement under her wings. She was a good mother, unduly anxious for the two young eaglets she had reared that season. Her mate, too, was a little more anxious than he had been in former years. Perhaps like Groonah, Greesha also remembered the spring of a year before when a moorland fire had destroyed their eyrie, and with it, the two young birds which were but a few weeks old.

As if in defiance of the grim fate that had brought disaster the previous mating season, Groonah had rebuilt the eyrie earlier than usual this year. By the beginning of March, it was ready. Sprigs of heather and stout roots of fern formed its foundation, with here and there a small shoot of aspen for decoration.

Unknown to Greesha, she had traveled far for the aspen twigs, for trees were few on Skye, and the only ones she knew of grew on the north part of the island. These aspens were, at their best, dwarfed saplings that had somehow managed to obtain roothold in a ravine.

During the second week of that same month, the first

of the eggs appeared in the nest; three days later, another lay beside it. The first was slightly smaller than the other, both, however, being brushed with reddish-yellow markings. Then commenced for Groonah her long vigil at the eyrie, lasting for almost six weeks. During the whole of that period, she was only absent from the site for short intervals. Greesha did most of the hunting for food, sleeping at night in a cleft some ten feet or so from where his mate brooded over her eggs.

For both birds, it was an anxious time. Snow fell at the heel of the month, and lay in heavy drifts on the hills and in the glens. The wind blew strongly from the north, and the watercourses were frozen over. Small tarns, the haunts of waterfowl, became mirrors of ice, and as a result, many a bird of the wader family helped fill the eagles' larder until the thaw came.

Once, when Greesha came sailing in with a hare clutched in his talons, he found his mate using her wings to sweep away a drift of snow that threatened to engulf the nest. When Groonah had first become aware of the danger, the drift lay in whorls on a cornice of the overhang that protected the eyrie from the northwest winds. By dragging one wing after the manner of an injured bird, she had managed to scoop away part of the main crust when Greesha joined her. Not long afterward, the overhang and the plateau above it were cleared completely, and the nest was no longer in danger.

During the incubation period, Groonah gave special attention to the smaller egg, sensing that it was of the utmost
importance that the young eaglet it contained broke through
before the other. Only then could the weaker bird hope to
survive.

When her long vigil drew to its end, she had the satisfaction of knowing that the male bird had indeed hatched
out before the female, and should, as time went on, be able
to protect himself against any assault his nesting partner
might make on him.

It had ever been thus with the Falconidae. Often the
female, the larger bird, survived at the expense of the male
unless, as Groonah had sensed, the male was born a little
in advance of the other.

No instinctive reasoning had guided Groonah, neither
was it a matter of logic that made her give special attention
to the smaller egg. She just sensed these things as had the
whole of her race before her. For endless centuries, she and
her kind had followed the same behavior patterns, each and
every one having been set by the simple process of trial and
error.

Thus, having successfully accomplished her purpose, with
her nestlings warm and contented beneath her pinions,
Groonah, on this night when the darkness came swiftly to
Bealach Mor, was strangely satisfied. She listened for her
mate's return from his hunting.

Suddenly Groonah raised her head and her neck feathers

stiffened a little. Out of the gloom a sound had come to her. She listened intently. Then she gave a low call so unlike the gruff bark usually associated with a bird of prey. A moment later, with a whoof of wings, Greesha alighted on the rock overhanging the eyrie, and dropped a mountain hare on to the ledge.

Groonah gave another soft call, then arranged herself more comfortably over the young eaglets, knowing that Greesha was settling down for the night in the cleft he habitually used as his roosting place.

Soon afterward, the wind rose, and the rain came. The silence of the eternal hills was broken by the sullen roar of burns in full spate.

The wind and the rain fought out their age-old battle in a darkness that completely hid the scene of conflict.

Groonah, sleepless on her mountain ledge, did not require the searching arrow of vision to tell her exactly what was happening out there on the moor.

The clouds, driving in like galleons wrecked on the rocks of the Trotternish tableland, were now breaking up in heavy rain over the storm-shapen crags of Roineval. The crevasses and gullys soon became foaming torrents that roared and shouted in unison with the winding bugle call of the West Wind whose home was far away in the wastes of the great ocean.

Groonah nestled down closer over the eaglets to give them

every possible protection from the probing fingers of the storm.

She was not unduly perturbed, merely a little over-cautious. No recurring act of memory was necessary for one such as she to recall the loss of her nestlings the previous year, and this time, she was leaving nothing to chance.

Thus she brooded over her young while the wind and the rain continued to battle in the darkness of the night, and the burns cried out as their burden of floodwater increased.

At last Groonah settled down to sleep. Less than an hour later, the wind blew itself out, and the broken ships of the storm drifted away with sails tattered and unfurling into thin streamers of mist until at last the stars shone through.

It grew perceptibly colder. Way off down the moor, a lamb bleated for its mother. Almost immediately, it was answered by the deep voice of the ewe herself. Scarcely a second later, a dark shape went loping down the moor toward the distant road. The rank, musky smell that lingered in the damp air betrayed the identity of the creature. It was Tawny-eye, the Bealach Mor fox, and now that the storm was past, he was off on another of his nocturnal journeys, alarming the lamb as he ran like a shadow past the sheep.

He paused for a few seconds by the bridge that carried the road over the burn. His stance, as he stood beside the low wall of the bridge, was that of an animal arrogant and cunning. At that hour of the night he had no fear as to his safety. Of all creatures of the wild, he was unrivaled when it came to treading the unknown paths that were the haunts of rabbits and less noticeable denizens of the shrub-land underworld.

After yawning and glancing up at the stars, which were now shining brightly as if mocking the storm that was past, he went slinking down a steep slope that led to a small croft in the vicinity of Inver Meadale.

His hunting that night would indeed be profitable. Not without sound reasoning governing his actions had he lazed away many a sunlit hour watching the crofter's hens.

Tawny-eye had learned long since how to take care of himself without expending too much energy while doing so.

Truly was he named "the red vagabond of the moor."

On Roineval, save for the constant roar of the burn in spate, it was very peaceful. After a time, the sullen noise of the tumbling water seemed to have become so much a part of the night as to be no longer of importance. It certainly did not disturb Groonah and her mate.

The hours passed by; the sky, just before daybreak, was little more than a black cloth that emphasized the movements of the stars, and the perceptible turn of the world toward the sun of a new day. Away in the north, a meteor fell swiftly toward the rim of the earth, leaving a trail of luminous vapor.

Then, just as the night was about to end, there came a bleating cry of fear, ending in a smothered gasp.

Groonah awakened, and raised her head a little to listen.
She knew exactly what had happened.

A sheep, heavy with rain-soaked fleece, had apparently
stumbled into a hollow and fallen on to its back. Before sunup,
it would be dead, having dislocated its neck in frantic efforts
to avoid slow suffocation.

For some minutes, the eagle heard the sheep continue the
struggle to regain its feet, heard the tempo quicken as fear
drove the stricken creature to greater effort. The sheep
coughed; then came a smothered groan, and Groonah knew
that she and her mate would not have to range far when the
dawn came. Fresh food for the eaglets would be available
less than a wing's thrust away.

The night and its stars faded. Then suddenly it was night
no longer. A new day had come.

CHAPTER TWO

THE SKY-RIDERS OF DRYNOCH

THE DAWN THAT MORNING CAME UP AS SUDDENLY AS THE darkness had come the night before. It was as though a covering of black velvet had been pulled from the surface of a silver mirror. Shortly afterward, the sun appeared, a huge, fiery ball bringing with it a brightness that was too strong to outlast the day.

Long before sunup, Greesha had launched himself from the rock pinnacle where he had spent the night. He noted the dead sheep some fifty yards away, hovered for a moment before rising in slow spirals over the moor. The ground tilted away at a crazy angle as he soared. Roineval, the Trotternish Mountains, the Cuillins, all were spread out beneath him. Beyond the conelike shapes of the Red Hills in the east, he could see the massed ranges of Wester Ross and Inverness-shire.

It was a grand world — this world of the eagles!

So many of their kind had looked down upon it as they soared into the sun; so many had seen it curving away to the remotest horizons so high had they risen above it. Possessing no enemy they themselves could not subdue, they had, many of them, lived long in the world, and recognized in the changing seasons the handiwork of the Great Spirit. Like all creatures of the wild, they knew that long before there had been mountains and glens, distant oceans and land-locked seas, there had been the Great Spirit who ruled all life wisely and well.

Greesha, however, felt no quickening in his blood because of the things that had existed from the very first sunrise when the world was new. Life, for him, was pure sensation — the sensation of flight. Everything he did was instinctive. He soared high because he and the wind were one. The feel of the air currents under his fanned tail or sliding past his wing tips roused in him an excitement that was the excitement of the entire Hawk family. The peregrine, the buzzard, the kestrel, down to the small merlin — all had a close affinity with the wind.

Higher and higher Greesha soared. The more widespread the scene below, the more sharply did he see with his miraculous eyes. Every detail was clear. Every shadow was no more than a skein of fine-spun silk on the heather and rocks, concealing nothing, but serving to reveal to the eagle's eye that which sought to remain hidden. From a height of two thousand feet, or more, he could see the movement of the tiniest vole, or the agitated flight of a crested tit over the few scattered boulders. As for rabbits, blue mountain hares, and grouse — his legitimate source of food supply — he could tell from the very spread of the heather, or slight break amidst the bog rushes, exactly where they were.

Even before the desire to hunt them down became manifest in his mind, they existed as a quick impression. Moreover, it was an impression as vivid as the alternating image of green earth and bright sky — of waving cotton grass and gold-tipped gorse — of rain-scarred gullys on the mountain slopes and the white clouds far above them.

Indeed, for Greesha and all of his kind, life was the swift fierceness of flight, born out of time, sensation rather than sharply defined action, pursuit in the place of predetermined strategy. Memory had little to do with an eagle's way of life. His whole world was too varied, too expansive to allow for recollection to dictate the mood of the immediate moment. All he knew was that to live, he must fly, and the rest came as a result of his being monarch of the air.

Thus, as Greesha soared high over Bealach Mor that morning, everything he experienced was compressed into sensation.

Suddenly he turned headlong into the wind, paused for a moment, then went into a stoop. With pinions pressed tightly against his body, he hurtled down like an immense stone. The ground, the craggy ridge of Roineval, leaped up to meet him in his tremendous fall earthward. Then he half spread his pinions and depressed the feathers in his fanlike tail. A second later, he swept over Roineval to surprise two hoodie crows who had been surveying the ridge and the eyrie.

Greesha was on them like a thunderbolt. The scavenging pair who, since the eaglets had been hatched, were always in the vicinity of the nest, scattered with cries of alarm.

The eagle flattened out when about fifty feet from the ground, and banking gracefully, floated leisurely along the small corrie, his enormous shadow preceding him across the moor below.

Sheep were grazing peacefully as he flew over them, and disclosed no sign of fear at the presence of the huge bird of prey. Neither Greesha nor Groonah were lamb killers — a charge often leveled against eagles without justification. The sheep that grazed on Bealach Mor, and the crofter who held the grazing rights, knew that the birds' hunting lay in other directions, and if, as did sometimes happen, the remains of a lamb were discovered in the nest, more often than not it was because a young ewe had failed in her duty and let the lamb fall into a gully and be killed. Once dead, the carcass would immediately attract the attention of the eagles who, unlike the hoodie crows, favored fresh meat. In a matter of minutes, the body would be retrieved from the gully and taken to the eyrie.

It was merely the ancient law of the wild at work.

As Greesha swung about in the wind and prepared to land close beside the ewe that had died in the night, the other sheep moved a little farther up the moorland. Dull-witted though they might be, they yet knew the stark shape of death when they saw it, and had no desire to witness the final stripping of what had been overtaken by the Great Mystery.

Only a motherless lamb stood bleating behind a boulder. Ever since daybreak it had stood thus, calling in a plaintive voice, and wondering why its mother refused to administer to its wants.

A very old ewe, lambless these three seasons past, came at a trot down the moor, and succeeded in focussing the attention of the motherless one on herself. Just as Greesha alighted and surveyed the hollow in which the dead sheep lay, the lamb ran from behind the rock, and began to follow the old ewe up the moor.

Greesha was not long in setting about his task of stripping the sheep. When he returned to the eyrie with the first choice morsels for the fledglings, he found that his mate had just finished feeding them the liver of the hare he had brought in the previous night.

Groonah looked up with satisfaction as he dropped lightly on to the small plateau of heather above the nest. She then started to preen her breast feathers while the young eaglets — small creatures of white down — gulped and blinked, and having eaten well, showed definite signs of wanting to go back to sleep.

A little over two weeks old, the young birds were not yet quite the size of ducks, their downy plumage tending to make them appear larger than they actually were. They already possessed voracious appetites and were constantly cheowping for food. As they sat in the nest, their crops filled to bulging point, they might have been owls, for there was clearly discernible about them the age-old look of wisdom so characteristic of all birds of prey.

Young though they were, they had quickly learned how best to protect themselves from the biting winds that often swept across the moor. Both made for the portion of the nest that sloped under the overhang, and before Groonah had completed her morning toilet, they were sound asleep.

By now, the sun was well up, but the sky was clouding over, and heavy banks of mist were dropping low over the main Cuillin ridge in the southeast. The water gullys on the western slopes of the range still showed a heavy run of water which, viewed from Roineval, had the appearance of quicksilver streaking the sides of the peaks.

Groonah, satisfied now that the eaglets had been fed and were once more asleep, suddenly opened her pinions and cast herself off the ledge. She glided for a moment up the corrie — a speckled-breasted creature of ineffable grace — then began to rise in slow, lazy spirals. That she was of greater size than her mate was evident from the moment she took to the air, yet because of it, she lacked none of the gracefulness that characterized Greesha. Moreover, she could, when occasion demanded, move even quicker than he by reason of her wider wing span.

When she had made her third turn in the sky, she was

aware that Greesha had joined her. She gave a gruff barklike sound in greeting, and the next instant, both birds were soaring higher and higher over Bealach Mor with never a wing-beat to aid them. They rode the air streams after the manner of their kind. This, for them, was effortless play — the game that all hawks had played since the first bird had soared to freedom in the wide arc of the sky.

They continued to wheel in mounting spirals until they passed through the first of the cloud masses streaming from off the Trotternish heights. Thrusting up even higher, they encountered more strongly the clean race of the wind from out of the magnetic north. They leaned on it, shaped their bodies to the rapid rhythm of its strumming; heard it shouting in their ears as it swept without ceasing over the shell of the earth. There was rain in it now, and the touch of ice. Sharp like a knife, it was yet ecstasy to the two birds. The wild tales it told of the ancient snowcaps of the north were tales all eagles had known for centuries back. Even the very scent of those far-off snowcaps was the cold breath of the Highlands which they had known ever since they glimpsed, with wondering eyes, the crags of their mountain stronghold.

As if seeking a wider and more profound knowledge than that which the wind possessed, the two eagles from Roineval continued to thrust up and up. The vapor whorls from the Trotternish went moving past, now with the birds, now far below until they became mere loops of mist and the eagles were themselves way up beyond both wind and cloud, soaring in a field of dazzling blue shot with the brightest of warm sunshine.

It was as though Greesha and Groonah were spiraling back into Time, into the first cosmic beginning of the universe.

Here — in the cradle of space — they were truly the greatest of living creatures. Famed in legend, they and their kind had been known to the philosophers of old as "Iolaire" and "Aquila," names familiar in the great network of the solar system and deemed worthy to be bestowed upon those of the eagle clan.

Small wonder then that the wing feathers of such birds had graced the headgear of kings and chieftains, that down through the long history of mankind, the eagle had ever been represented as the true monarch of the wild. So regal a creature was he that his likeness, as a symbol of power and nobility, was found engraved on coin and banner, and with the dawning of the Age of Wisdom, saints and craftsmen endeavored to shape out of precious metals another such as he to support in their temples the Book of Life!

High above the cloud-wrapped world of moor and loch, Greesha and Groonah wheeled and turned, the eternal symphony of space being for them the voice of the Great Spirit itself.

As a result, all joy and knowledge was theirs, and it was a knowledge inherited from those who had come from out of the ancient years when the first mountain crag gave refuge to a bird of prey and the clarion call of the first eagle went echoing through the dim and silent corridors of the glens.

Back on the eyrie, the young eaglets lay silent in sleep. Their tiny digestive organs were already at work, passing into the vital parts of their quickening bodies the nourishment contained in the food their mother had so recently given them.

Only the persistent buzzing of a few early flies disturbed the quietness of the nest.

Not many minutes later, a bar of warm sunlight crept toward the fledglings — Nature, too, was preparing to do her part in assisting to rear them.

CHAPTER THREE

WATCHERS OF THE WILD

THE MORNING WAS STILL YOUNG WHEN TAWNY-EYE CAME loping along the bank of the burn, carrying his red brush at a jaunty angle. Having feasted well on a couple of plump hens he had succeeded in stealing from the croft at Inver Meadale, his mask was wrinkled with the suggestion of a grin as if in satisfaction at the way he had bested the crofter's old sheep dog.

Jock had been asleep in his kennel when Tawny-eye came creeping up out of the night toward the outbuildings. So as not to disturb the dog whom he had scented while still some distance away, the fox, with great cunning, had gone back a little on the trail, finally approaching his objective from a more northerly direction.

Tawny-eye had always been one to make good use of his natural gifts of scent and cunning, and on this particular occasion, his resourcefulness had served him well. In fact, his raid on the hencoop had been carried out in complete silence. Jock had slept on undisturbed, all because Tawny-eye, the most cunning of hunters, had kept to the leeward of the animal.

The satisfaction he felt at the exploit gave the jaunty tilt to his brush as the fox came back up the moor. Moreover, he was happy in the knowledge that it was easy to live well without having to course, half the night, creatures who, all too often, were as swift as he.

Tawny-eye panted as he followed the endless twists and turns of the burn, moving with assurance over the ground. There was not a single strategic point that he did not know as well as the terrain surrounding his lair. The shape of every hill he knew; the lay of every tarn. Even the small underground streams that, many a year since, had followed their ancient runnels beneath the earth finally to pour into deep potholes hidden beneath tufts of coarse heather. Yes, indeed! Tawny-eye knew. He was as wise as he was cunning!

Although he had no conception of time, the fox was certainly well aware that he had dwelt almost all his life in this district of rock and burn. The springs, summers, autumns and winters he had known on the moor were but milestones in his life, each recording the rise and decline of but another year. As yet, there was no frost of age in his limbs to warn him that the sands of his own existence were fast running out as the changing seasons blossomed and died.

Happy in his ignorance of such things, and a vagabond by choice, he went from day to day full of confidence in his own capabilities, and caring not a bit that he was a parasite in this world of the wild.

This was his fifth year on Bealach Mor, and long since he

had forgotten the place where he had been born, way over on the Trotternish range. There had been three others like him, all with a streak of laziness in their natures which they had undoubtedly inherited from the old dog fox who had sired them.

While Tawny-eye had no memory of those who had been his brothers, he yet had vague, sometimes disturbing, dream pictures of old Torn-ear, his sire. Maybe it was because the wily old fox had given to Tawny-eye, more than to the others, many of those same characteristics that he himself had possessed.

Of the vixen who had been his mother, Tawny-eye had no memory at all. She might never have existed for all the influence she had left on him. Yet, she had fed him while her mate lazed away many of the hours that should have been spent providing for his family. Perhaps it was because she had to travel so far afield to supply the young cubs' wants that one day she went off, and becoming reckless, failed to return.

The manner of her departure had been quite uneventful. She just set off when the afternoon was growing deep in shadow with the westering sun glowing redly above the hills.

For a long time the cubs had waited patiently for her to return, Tawny-eye, because he was hungry, finally leaving the lair to sit motionless outside so he could be the first to see her when she did eventually put in an appearance.

The hours passed by until the moon began to ride the summits of the hills — a full moon it was that night — and the young fox grew afraid as the rocks surrounding the lair took on fantastic shapes. Then a little breeze from off the distant sea whimpered in the gully below the den, stirring the few rowan bushes until the night was filled with many strange sounds.

There had been something unreal about the gully then — the rowans dwarfed and twisted through constant battling with the wind, and the boulders seeming almost to rise up and move in a little closer in the slow-gathering moonglow.

Even now — in this, his fifth year of vagabondage on Bealach Mor — Tawny-eye was aware of a deepening distrust within him when he heard bushes whispering and crying in the wind. Yet, even as he had no memory of the vixen who had reared him and had suddenly gone off never to return, neither had he memory of the rowans and the gully where he had been born. Only the whispering together of the whins and the heather when stirred by the breeze, and the sharp outline of rocks etched against the moonlight, revealed a little of what had been lost in the obscure depths of his animal mind.

All that persisted now of those far-off, forgotten days, was the dream vision of old Torn-ear leading him down over the rough, stony ground to this — the wastes of Bealach Mor where he had remained ever since.

No doubt that long, long ago, Torn-ear had followed the vixen, his mate, into the Great Unknown which awaited all animals of the wild on the shores of the dark loch at World's End.

Perhaps, because the cub he had brought down off the Trotternish heights to Bealach Mor had much to learn of the vagrant ways of the wild, the Great Unknown who dwelt on the shores of the dark loch at World's End had taken compassion on the old fox who had sought to aid at least one of his offspring. Maybe, as a result, only his aging body had been demanded of the old rogue, and his indolent spirit, naked and frightened, sent back to join the cub and remain with him until he too trod the track to the dark loch.

One thing was certain! Tawny-eye was the very image of his sire, and every bit as lazy. Even his annoyance at the stonechats, who repeatedly uttered their warning cries as he trotted along the bank of the burn, had been annoyance similarly expressed by old Torn-ear.

The twittering cries of the small birds increased in volume as Tawny-eye pressed on up the moor, and finally reached the track that led to the hollow where the dead sheep lay. Within a matter of seconds, the wind brought to his nostrils the smell of the fresh meat.

He paused, right foreleg raised. His wet nose tested the air currents. He then left the course of the burn and made for the hollow in which the sheep was lying. He stood staring, his jaws gaping in anticipation.

The next moment, he was conscious of two wide-pinioned

shadows sweeping over him. Groonah and Greesha had come to safeguard what they considered theirs alone.

The fox, despite his lazy nature, was not a coward. Nevertheless, he was not prepared to face the wrath of two irate eagles. He knew that they could soar high above him, then, with a downward swoop, be on him in the twinkling of an eye and crush the life out of his body with one grip of their mighty talons.

As he glanced up apprehensively, he saw both birds encircling the depression and decided, with relief, that they were more inclined to drive him off than to make a concentrated attack upon him. Tawny-eye was quick to sense that discretion was the better part of valor in this instance and, as the birds dipped to make yet another wide turn, he leaped out of the hollow and took refuge behind an immense boulder.

The two eagles, having achieved their purpose in driving the red-coated one from the sheep, were no longer interested in him. They flew back to the plateau above the eyrie where they stood watching the hollow.

The fox interpreted correctly their attitude toward him and made off across the glen, giving an occasional backward glance to ensure that he was not being pursued.

Leaping across a narrow neck of the burn, he set up a rabbit. In a moment, he was transferred from an idle, loping creature into an animal sure of foot and quick to attack. The unfortunate rabbit fell an easy victim to Tawny-eye's prowess, and the fox feasted there and then, knowing full well that the eagles would not dispute his right to anything he had killed himself.

When Tawny-eye finally moved on, making a detour to reach his lair on the opposite side of the glen, cloud masses began to gather over Bealach Mor, and soon the sun was completely hidden. Even as the last of the sunshine went leaping down toward Loch Harport, over the heights of the Trotternish, the mists were dropping quickly. Rain was not far off. A keen wind, too, was rising, sweeping down over the now gray moor like a bodiless creature seeking something tangible upon which to vent its spite.

Tawny-eye met the full force of it as he came out on to a high ridge that marked the southeastern boundary of Glen Vidigill. At a point where two small burns met and fell in a foaming cascade into a rock basin, a peewit called out, then rose in agitated flight.

The old fox wondered what had disturbed the bird. He then saw, lower down, that two sheep were engaged in combat, one making a very determined effort to overthrow his opponent. Just when it seemed he was near to succeeding, a lamb ran bleating up the glen.

In an instant the sheep ceased their struggling, and then began to make off toward higher ground. The movement they glimpsed way off down the moor warned them that a shepherd and his dog were approaching in their direction.

Tawny-eye still remained motionless on the ridge, his gaze centred on the sheep. Just then, the first of the two eagles left the nesting site, having become aware of the shepherd moving slowly up the moor. The bird flew low, flapping its way across the glen. Then it turned and continued straight along the summit of the opposite ridge of hills, banking slightly where the two burns met above the falls.

At the very moment when the bird banked, a gleam of sunlight broke through the massing clouds. It leaped quickly along the line of the hills, and the eagle changed from black to bronze. The slow rhythmic beating of those powerful pinions carried him with ease down the deep cleft of the valley toward the loch. Then he began to soar until he became a speck in the sky.

A few seconds later, Groonah also launched herself from the nest and followed the course taken by Greesha.

It was then that Tawny-eye began to suspect that something was amiss. The stonechats were calling all up the glen. Two hoodie crows, who till then had been skulking along the shoulder of Roineval, made off clumsily, croaking as they flew.

In the meantime, the shepherd and his dog turned off into a narrow defile. Before the man had again emerged on to the open moor, he was calling out instructions to his dog. The animal sped away at his bidding to round up some sheep who were to be segregated from the rest of the flock for shearing.

The sharp words of command reached Tawny-eye, and he knew then why the stonechats were calling out and the eagles had made off down the glen.

Sinking low to the ground, the fox started to make for his lair and, not long afterward, was fast asleep where man could never find him, his forepaws tucked up under his red ruff, and his brush curled around the tip of his nose.

Meanwhile, the shepherd and his dog continued methodically with their task and soon began to move off down the moor, driving part of the flock to the shearing and dipping pen down by the road.

A scud of rain broke over the distant rim of hills. Already Ben Duagrich in the northwest was blotted out. The clouds were coming in low, trailing ragged and broken over the rocky outcrops. On Roineval itself, some of the higher crags were losing their shapes as the mist engulfed them.

Somewhere — not far off — a buzzard called plaintively. The mewling notes of its mate sounded muffled across the glen.

Then from the eyrie came a shrill clamoring: "Cheeowp! Cheeowp!" The young eaglets were calling the old birds.

They continued to cry; and it was the complaining of hungry fledglings who knew how best to attract the attention of those who provided for them.

Almost at once, Groonah and Greesha glided out from amidst the clouds, flying at an altitude of some seventy feet.

They came on silently, and without movement of their huge pinions. So slow did the flight appear to be that it was little short of marvelous the ease with which they sailed through the air. So low were they that every detail of the birds was clearly visible — their speckled breasts, the upturned feathers on their wing tips and, typical of their kind, the restrained power that accompanied their progress toward the nest.

The young eaglets were calling more loudly now — a curious sound for such enormous creatures as they would one day be. It was clear that they were aware of the old birds' approach.

Then the mist covered the entire ridge that was Roineval, and with it, the rain — Groonah and her mate flying without hesitation into the steaming vapor and vanishing as silently as they had appeared.

The fledglings ceased to cry; the old birds were once again on the nest!

A sheep bleated way out on the moor; again came the distant mewling of the buzzards. A stonechat set up a ceaseless piping, to be joined by others farther down the glen. When these sounds finally ceased, only the burn sang out, soon to be accompanied by the high treble of the wind fluting amidst the crags and driving before it the silver-arrowed rain from the west.

CHAPTER FOUR

THE SAGA OF TAWNY-EYE

The First Phase

ON THAT MORNING WHEN THE BRIGHT DAWN ENDED IN heavy rain, and Tawny-eye lay curled asleep in his earth, there became enmeshed in his life the first threads that were eventually to snare and overthrow him. Lazy though he was, insolent as he had always been, these very traits in his character were to become highroads leading toward an end as glorious as it was unselfish.

Groonah was to be the harbinger of the great destiny that had now become his.

Nobody was to know of the events that led finally to Tawny-eye's battle with Groonah, and his seemingly ignoble defeat and exit from the scene of his former triumphs.

All any eyes were to see was the red-coated one's death — a death the fox seemed well to deserve since he had become an incorrigible thief. To all of the small animal community on Bealach Mor, Tawny-eye was known for just a good-for-nothing vagabond who would, in due course, come to a bitter end.

Nevertheless, it was a great day in the life of Tawny-eye — this day of heavy rain that was the beginning of his glorious saga!

So few outstanding events in the lives of wild creatures have begun on so wild and desolate a day. Yet, at no other time could reynard's destiny have been set in motion. The leaping, boisterous wind, the cold, driving rain, were but a few of the strands that were soon to become merged into a clearly arranged pattern. Even the low drifting clouds, and the shouting burns, had a part in it. So, too, had the mountain ridge of Roineval, and the mists which repeatedly covered its crags and ledges.

The only tragic thing about it all was that Tawny-eye himself had no preconceived knowledge of the part he was to play as hero in a futile cause.

He awakened from his heavy sleep a little after midday. Hearing the whimpering of the wind outside his rocky shelter, and sensing that it was raining, he curled himself into a more closely knit ball of fur, intending to sleep on. The wind, however, found its way into his lair. It ruffled his magnificent coat; it tickled his ears, and, speaking to him in a language he knew and understood, told him of the rain-drenched wastes beyond his door where hunting was good and where the Spirit of Fur and Feather awaited him.

The old fox of many season's experience found that it was impossible to sleep. He was filled with a strange, recurring restlessness.

"Wheeoo! Wheeoo!" cried the wind in a voice that was so like the calling of young buzzards at play.

Tawny-eye felt compelled to listen.

It seemed to say: "Come out! Come out, lazy one. The whole of Bealach Mor is for your pleasure today."

At last the fox obeyed the insistent entreaty of the wind, and stretching tardily, gave a grunt and shook himself. A moment later he emerged from the lair to see if the wind spoke the truth.

Indeed, it was no lie he had been told. The whole of the moor, as far as he could see, was desolate with a desolation that only wind and rain can bring. Sheep, which were usually scattered far and wide, intent on their grazing, were, for the most part, huddled together beneath the massive outcrops.

Tawny-eye sniffed the air, then glanced down the glen. The prospect was not altogether pleasing. The burn was once again in full spate, and the fox knew that the bogs would be deepest on the lower reaches of the moor.

He accordingly turned his gaze in the direction of the high ground beyond the Vidigill Burn in the north. Hesitant though he was, he sensed that he would be traveling north that day. There was something in the wind that attracted him — a vague scent he tried hard to unravel; and he felt that he would only come to it if he headed uphill toward Beinn Totaig.

When he did eventually move off, he loped slowly. Then

he quickened his pace, crossed in a single leap the burn that wound around to Roineval, and was soon traversing the high stretch of moorland known as Monadh Meadale. Not long afterward, he was ascending the slopes of Beinn Totaig without undue effort.

The wind and the rain were in his face; but he did not mind. For all its blustery wildness, the wind was clean and fresh, leaving the scent of heather and bracken in a lingering fusion as it rushed down from the mountains. As for the rain, in spite of the fact that on the exposed crags it fell with a sharp-edged severity, in the hollows of the glen it was fine and soft. Lower down the moor, in the small clefts which the wind somehow missed, it was little more than a drifting vapor like the breath of a sigh dissolving quietly.

On the trail, however, which Tawny-eye followed, visibility was poor. The fox was running with nose to the wind, and eyes half-closed because of the moisture that was trickling down from his head. He was therefore shocked into complete immobility when a dark shape hurtled down ahead of him. Before he could quite grasp what had happened, the shape rose, a grouse clutched in death-dealing talons.

The eagle's swoop on her prey had been utterly silent; silent, too, the death of the grouse she had slain instantaneously. Quivering with sudden fear, Tawny-eye half crouched as Groonah, having made her kill, swooped up over him and headed back to the eyrie on Roineval.

In the quick, nervous glance that he gave, Tawny-eye

could see plainly the dead game bird gripped in the eagle's right foot. A million, million reflexes in reynard's mind recorded indelibly the sureness of the kill and Groonah's swift surge upward. Groonah, the Golden Eagle of Roineval, had now his role assigned. The fox was never to forget that grouse that she was carrying back to her fledglings!

Notwithstanding, before the eagle had reached the nest, the fox was again on his way — the entire incident seemingly forgotten — following what to him just then was far more important — that queer, tantalizing stain on the wind.

It was stronger now as he approached the summit of Beinn Totaig. Oblivious to the dampness of his head and back, he grew excited. The blood raced through his veins. Already he was sensing the presence of what sent out the taint in the wind. He exulted for a moment in the knowledge that increased with the wild singing of his turbulent blood.

At last Tawny-eye reached the crest and stood leaning against the wind, listening. Down below, he could see a dark tarn, and in a deep cleft, the southern run of the Vidigill Burn. The Glen of the River, as the cleft was known, was, on this day of heavy rain, more like the Ravine of the Torrent, for the burn was white with froth and flowing swiftly.

Tawny-eye became suddenly taut with excitement. The wind had dropped for an instant; then coming up again, this time from the north, it brought more strongly than ever the taint which had enticed the fox well up the glen to this isolated hill above the tarn. Testing the air eagerly, he could now identify the scent. It was that of a vixen, and it came from the small cairn of stones that marked the summit height. Stiff-legged, and with his brush well raised, Tawny-eye trod forward cautiously, and in as many heartbeats as would make up a minute, came at last to a small cavern under the stones wherein Biod — the vixen with the yellow back — had crawled to die.

Without looking one way or the other, old reynard stood side-long to the dark entrance to the cairn. No sound did he make; no movement of either eye or muscle disturbed the rigidity of his body. He knew, without reasoning, that the vixen sheltering beneath the cairn was watching him as he stood motionless where the wind and the rain made sport on the barren summit of the hill.

Then, for a moment, shorter than the intake of her breath, Biod seemed to see him more clearly. The hand of Nature had stayed, for a fraction, the scud of the rain before the wind, and outside her refuge, the striking fantasy of light so often manifest on high hills gave Tawny-eye a girth and majesty of form he did not really possess.

Biod gave a low whine in her throat, and her eyes gleamed a little tragically when Tawny-eye gave no sign of response. She sensed that he was waiting for her to leave the shelter under the cairn and join him. This, unfortunately, she was unable to do. In fact, during the past two days, it had become quite clear to her that she would never move again. She was paralyzed!

Even as she gazed at Tawny-eye, standing so firmly on legs she guessed were quick in movement, the memory of her own terrible affliction brought renewed desperation to her heart.

Till then, she had lain in a stupor. Now, the sight of one of her kind standing so serenely out there in the world she would never tread again, filled her with a terror that made her relive in a single flash of time the disaster that had brought her low.

Memory, with her, was a thing of dread, deep-seated in a darkness that was the darkness of her slowly approaching fate. As the scene where she had met with such grave misfortune flashed across the screen of her consciousness, every single incident became vitally alive once more. She saw, as sharply as if she were treading the hills again, the broken, jagged rocks of Beinn Mheadhonach, reflected in the dark eye of the tarn at the foot of Beinn Totaig. Then coming up from out of the sunset was the creature she knew to be herself — vibrant with life — the dark-hued brush half-curled over a yellow back.

Yet another quick change of scene revealed herself with body full-stretched, preparing with eagerness to trap the rabbit that was sitting so unconcerned on a ledge that cut diagonally across the largest of the rocks. The leap, too, she made was there with her as she lay helpless under the cairn. She could almost feel the swift thrust of her now useless legs that had carried her over the crag — a thrust badly calculated, for she missed the ledge and the rabbit, falling with a heavy thud on to her back some twelve feet below.

Biod screamed out with fright as memory made vivid the hour and place of her destruction, but no pain now did she feel — nothing! The badly injured back and legs were already dead, and pain only a thing that dwelt in the dark corners of her mind. CO. SCHOOLS C625507

Of her slow recovery from the shock she had experienced, of the long, ceaseless struggle she had made up the slopes of Beinn Totaig, memory no longer retained any distinct image. She only knew of the darkness of the lair she had finally found under the cairn. Oddly enough, memory had also lost its hold on the long hours she had spent while paralysis deadened pain, and day changed to night and back to day again.

Before the last of the lightninglike impressions faded in her brain, a new glow leaped into Biod's eyes. There was a movement outside the lair as Tawny-eye, tired of posing, turned and began to sniff his way toward the place where the vixen lay hidden. The old fox crouched down on all fours the better to peer into the den. Biod whined, then the next thing she knew Tawny-eye was sniffing her; his muzzle was moving lightly over her head and shoulders.

The wind soughed in the scrub above Monadh Meadale. Way over, across the Vidigill Burn, stern Roineval brooded in its crown of mist. Nothing stirred on the crags that were swept by the driving rain. Not even a young eaglet cheoowped with discomfort. No sheep called. No buzzard uttered its plaintive cry. Only down by the dark tarn that was Loch Vidigill was there any sign of life, and that was the sound of snipe rising, their wings whirring, and their necks outstretched as they flew. When they had gone, only the falling of the rain in the tarn made music. For the rest, it seemed a long, long day, and many hours must still pass until, behind the wind and rain, came the darkness.

Time, on Bealach Mor, was a slow-moving thing, heavy-heeled, and of no importance.

Rascal though he was, Tawny-eye had instincts that would have befitted a domestic animal better than one living so wild and careless a life. Those same instincts told him on his first acquaintance with Biod that all was not well with her. The lay of her body in the lair with hind legs stretched out to their fullest extent puzzled him. Then he knew that they were dead, useless things, those legs of hers — cold with a coldness he associated with sticks long since fossilized by the action of rain upon rain for more seasons than he and his kind had known. He remembered one such stick he had found up on Roineval. When he tried to pick it up in his jaws, he found he could not move it.

Somehow, Tawny-eye arrived at the conclusion that Biod's legs were the same. Something else, too, he knew. The vixen was hungry. The dull look in her eyes told him that. He sensed that he would have to hunt for her.

After nuzzling her once again, the old fox of a hundred cunning ways withdrew from the lair and headed off down the hill, traveling toward the tarn and the long tussocky grass where he knew rabbits would be hidden. As he swung off the hill into the hollow, the wind and the scud of rain passed high over his back. Above the tarn itself, the rain was little more than a mist, so exactly like the mist in the little gullys on the far side of the hill near his home.

Tawny-eye shook the moisture from his coat, then began stalking, his body low to the ground, his nose testing the air, and his red brush curled like a banner over his left flank.

A brace of snipe rose from the rushes as he came up close to the tarn. A mallard that had crouched hidden near a boulder stretched his wings and skimmed the surface of the dark sheet of water.

Before the drake had reached the opposite shore, Tawny-eye had pounced on something squatting in a spot where the tussocky grass grew sparse and tall. One squeal the creature gave as reynard's jaws closed on the back of its neck. Even before life had actually left it, Tawny-eye had turned, the body limp in his mouth. His brush waved as he carried the young leveret up the hill to the cairn where Biod lay waiting.

Tawny-eye hunted much that day. The lair under the rocks now contained, in addition to the leveret, three rabbits and the half-skinned leg of a lamb which had died and had been partially stripped by both eagles and buzzards.

The old fox, however, was a trifle harassed. Biod had made

no great effort to eat what he had brought. True she had picked at the leg of the lamb, but was sick soon afterward.

Tawny-eye felt it a matter of expediency that he should bring her something likely to tempt her appetite. He therefore continued to course the haunts of those creatures that lived by the tarn, ignoring now the rabbits and seeking something quite different.

Backward and forward he went, but keeping always close to the fringe of the tarn. This place, he sensed, was the wind-loved world of many creatures. A grouse flew up almost from beneath his very feet. The rushes dipped and swayed close to where he stood. The water of the tarn rippled a little, its ebony darkness changing for a second until it was a warm brown color — a golden brown like the plumage of the eagles on Roineval.

Then reynard saw it — a tremulous shadow in the rushes bordering the water's edge. One shattering squawk it uttered as he caught it — a grouse with a broken wing — the mate of the one that had flown away. As in the case of the blue leveret he had slain earlier, Tawny-eye was soon away up the hill, conscious that at last he had something Biod, the paralyzed vixen, would eat.

Even as he departed like a twisting shadow among the boulders, night came up from across the glen, and with it, sweeter than the rain-soaked scent of heather, the smell of a little wood smoke borne on the wind from some distant crofter's hearth fire. The rain clouds began to break up over the

Trotternish glen. The last of the hidden sun flickered for a while behind the drift of mist. Far over, by Loch Harport, a light gleamed out for an instant, twinkled, then was gone, like a candle suddenly lit and as suddenly extinguished.

In the southeast, the rocky slopes of the Cuillins were hidden in vapor that eddied like white smoke across the glens. Only the peak of Blaven stood clear above the clouds, staring like some blind-eyed sphinx at Loch Scavaig and the far-off hills of Rhum.

CHAPTER FIVE

RASHUAL

THE NIGHT WITNESSED A CHANGE IN THE DIRECTION OF THE wind. It ceased to blow from the northwest, and an hour after midnight came in from the southeast, bringing to the Highlands a spell of fine, sunny weather. The last of the rain clouds broke up on the mainland peaks, and went flying like ragged banners across the wide valley of the Spey to become lost in the wastes of Wester Ross and Sutherland. A new moon was born in the welter of streaming cloud, and when the sky was clear, shone like a sickle of silver, lying on its back and sinking westward.

Groonah saw it as she brooded her young on the eyrie on Roineval. Tawny-eye saw it, too, as he lay close to the cairn on Beinn Totaig, satisfied in the knowledge that the vixen had eaten the grouse he had killed the previous evening.

Greesha was off on his hunting long before the sun came up. As he turned into the wind and suddenly soared upward, he reveled in the bite of the air, seeing, as he turned, a gray world spinning toward the edge of the sunrise. Tilting away from him was the moorland riding up to the mountain ridges, and the burns crisscrossing silver-white as the new day seemed to spill out from the night that was going. Greesha it was who heard the voice of the first cuckoo calling across the glen of Monadh Meadale as the sun glowed beyond the rim of the hills on the mainland.

Spring had certainly come in all its singing splendor to Bealach Mor, spreading all over the Isle of Skye. Fish rose in Vidigill Burn, while down on Loch Harport, sea trout broke surface in sudden scurries that sent wide ripples breaking against the inward swinging tide. Where the water ebbed clear and deep, schools of jellyfish gleamed purple and transparent. Flying above them were the sea gulls from the bay below Bracadale, twisting and turning like pieces of paper blown by a contrary wind.

All these things Greesha saw as he sailed high over the moor. Then he commenced to hunt in earnest, going into stoop after stoop over his intended victims. The sun had been scarce an hour over the horizon before the nest on Roineval was replenished with fresh meat for the eaglets. Loud indeed were the complaints when Groonah flew up to the rock she and her mate had turned into a larder. The eaglets knew that she had food hidden away.

Groonah was exceedingly careful in arranging their diet. She tore at the flesh of the tenderest rabbits, carrying down to the eaglets those morsels she knew would benefit them most. Both birds were voracious in their demands on her, and more than once danced up and down the nest when she attempted to leave them.

At last Groonah decided that she had given them sufficient attention for the time being. While there was no desire on her part to neglect them, she certainly had no intention to encourage their every whim.

For a while longer, Groonah sat on the small plateau above the nest. She became busily engaged in preening her breast feathers, completely ignoring the young birds who, now that they were well fed, just squatted with crops full, staring away across the glen until sleep overtook them and they lay together as if for warmth.

Groonah did not so much as glance at them when she finally glided off the plateau and, with widespread pinions, joined Greesha and began to frolic over the expanse of Loch Harport where the sea trout were now swimming against the ebbing tide.

Up beyond the head of the loch, the black shape of a hooded crow caught Greesha's attention. As he swung about, the better to watch the crow's line of flight, Groonah called to him.

Greesha responded to his mate's inviting call, thrusting up immediately toward her. A second later, the crow had vanished, swooping down on to a stretch of pasture situated just above the Drynoch river. His hour of meeting with Greesha was not yet!

Meanwhile, high above the loch, coming up from the sea, was a solan goose. Groonah had caught sight of it the moment it crossed the coastline. As her mate soared and joined her, the goose swerved, its long neck stretched out to its fullest extent, its wings beating rapidly.

The two eagles spiraled, watching . . .

The goose had seen the sea trout, moving forward in a mass against the tide. Something else, however, he did not see — a bulkhead of timber almost motionless where held by the ebbing currents. For him, only the gleam of silver where fish were riding now the downward surge of water . . .

No sound came from the goose as he checked his line of flight and hung for a second almost directly below the two eagles who were spiraling downward in his direction. An instant later, coinciding with an undercurrent from the Meadale Burn that sent the bulkhead of timber swinging right amidst the trout, the goose dropped like a stone.

So swiftly did he fall that the fish were gone before he was aware of it, and his enormous beak struck the piece of timber with a resounding crash.

For a few minutes as Greesha and Groonah encircled the spot, nothing could be seen but ever-widening ripples and a small whirlpool on the surface of the loch. Then as the timber came once again into sight, floating lopsided, the goose was little more than a mass of bedraggled feathers, his neck broken and his beak wedged firmly in the bulkhead that rose and fell as the tide continued to ebb.

The two eagles flew slowly over the spot, and deciding

that they could not get hold of the goose without danger to themselves, thrust upward into the veering wind, and were soon little more than specks in a mackerel sky.

About the same hour when Groonah left the eyrie on Roineval to join her mate over Loch Harport, some two miles across the moor in the direction of Drynoch, two evil-looking hoodie crows were bickering at one another. Finally, the male bird, Rashual, launched himself off the outcrop where he and his mate roosted. Making a wide sweep over the moor, he headed down a narrow glen that opened out on to the loch.

Rashual was in a very bad humor. His mate had been particularly quarrelsome that morning, and he was glad to be off on his own for a while.

As he approached the upper reaches of the loch he saw long runnels of water below, where peat had been cut. They were, to him, watercourses he knew very well indeed, for often had he searched for carrion on their banks. He was about to dive down when a current of air lifted him a little, and as he turned, he came into sight of a snug little croft perched on the edge of a lush meadow. Sheep were in an adjacent enclosure, and at the rear of the building were some hens.

Rashual encircled the dwelling, then flattening out a little, again approached the homestead at a much lower elevation, unaware that he had been, momentarily, under the keen observation of Greesha. He was, in fact, sharply focused in the eagle's eye just as the current of air lifted him out of his course.

By the time he was conscious of the croft, Greesha had joined his mate, and the danger that had existed was past.

From the height at which the crow now flew, the building and the small fenced-off fields were seen in a different perspective, and all moving creatures assumed a distinct shape and significance. He had not eaten that day, and was hungry. Nevertheless, he had no serious intention of ravaging the croft livestock until he saw some young chicks on the extreme edge of the pasture.

A vivid reflex in his brain brought to life the familiar image of the eaglets' nest on Roineval; then the nest and the young birds were forgotten as, indulging in another wide sweep, he once more came in low over the croft. This time, he headed straight for the edge of the pasture where the chicks were running to and fro.

The crow came to rest but a few yards away. He stood ready to pounce, his eyes searching out the largest and plumpest of the brood. That hesitation on his part served him no good purpose. The hen — mother of the chicks — saw him as he stood with wings half spread. She was on him in a trice — a small creature compared to Rashual — but one that was a tornado of fury in her anxiety to protect her young. She made a tremendous outcry as she went straight for the crow, and the chicks, suddenly aware of danger, began to scatter in all directions.

Rasual poised himself ready to meet her. Abandoning all thought of the chicks, he decided to make off with the hen herself. He lunged forward, his vicious beak ready to strike. His talons, too, were extended but only to aid him in gripping the ground.

Shrieking loudly, the hen flew over his head, but had already turned to face him as he whirled around to make a further attack on her.

The crow was now fully roused. One fierce stab he made at her, his beak striking her in the eye. The hen gave an agonized squawk and shook her head. Rashual splayed his wings slightly the better to press home the attack.

He was not quick enough. The hen fluttered out of reach, and Rashual saw the swift movement of the crofter's dog in his direction.

With a croak of fear, the crow spread his wings for the take-off. He was less than a foot off the ground when the sheltie leaped. Rashual gave another croak, this time of acute pain. The dog had snapped at his outstretched legs and failed to get a grip; but he had broken the skin, and as Rashual made off, badly frightened, he was conscious of having escaped a serious disaster. He flew straight to his nesting site, and was quite prepared to continue his never-ending quarrel with his mate.

To his disgust, Rashual found the nest deserted when he arrived at the outcrop. Because of the hurt in his legs, he found it difficult to roost comfortably. Since there was no sign of his mate, he grew more sullen than ever. His recent escape from the fangs of the sheep dog was no longer a thing of importance. He was now disturbed by the quietness and by the absence of his mate who had never failed to return to the outcrop immediately he himself put in an appearance.

Rashual grumbled in his throat, and started to preen his feathers savagely, trying in vain to get at the insects which irritated his skin.

Suddenly he heard a buzzard wailing above him. He saw the bird swoop out from a wisp of cloud, and then begin to glide in the wind currents, so like Groonah whom he had grown to hate.

Rashual ceased his vicious searching for the insects that troubled him, and raised himself on the nest. He blinked as he remembered the eaglets who were so much larger than the young chicks that had enticed him on to the croft meadow.

As he continued to stare upward, he saw that the buzzard had almost vanished from sight, sailing swiftly on the downward currents of the high, swinging wind.

Rashual shook himself. Being familiar with the vagaries of the Falconidae, he guessed that Groonah and her mate would be absent from the eyrie just now, probably indulging in their love of the wind as was the buzzard which had just passed overhead. The wind had always been something the eagles and their kind could not resist.

Just when his mate came flying up toward the outcrop, Rashual left the nest, heading direct for the heights of Roineval.

Close to the cleft of the burn, the spring whins and gorse, now so fresh and green, rustled in the breeze. There were sudden scurryings in the long grass as small creatures hustled about their business of living. The smart and dainty little stonechats called constantly "wee-chat — wee-chat-chat." Here and there they could be seen in pairs flitting over the burn, their plumage of chestnut pink and dark brown bringing a sudden blaze of color to the dead grass that lay withered in the cracks and lichen-gray hollows of the boulders.

Two little crested tits with black bibs and collars sat on the top of a rock, twittering gaily. They appeared exceptionally happy, enjoying the sun.

A tree pipit, without a nesting place, stood forlorn on a sprig of gorse, and peered with bright eyes at the crested tits. He alone of the birds beside the burn was on the alert. Having no mate, and as a result no domestic problems, his time was less occupied in having to search for food. Thus he often stood and watched others, and of all the birds in the region of the burn, knew much of what was happening in the locality.

Suddenly, as if tiring of being so inactive when others were so busy, he flew off to the point where the shattered stakes of an old sheep fence led direct to the corrie below the eagles' eyrie. Alighting on one of the stakes, he viewed the rugged ridge of Roineval, marking each crag that was so sharply defined against the skyline.

Sunlight fell warm and comforting upon him as it did upon the red shape of the fox standing motionless on a small grassy hummock scarcely fifty yards away. Reynard was staring up intently at Roineval which seemed a most deserted place.

Quite suddenly Roineval no longer seemed completely deserted. A large, black bird appeared on the topmost rocks of the ridge. It gave a raucous call, and was promptly answered by another of the same species. The tree pipit flew a few feet above the watching fox, causing him to leap forward.

Rashual saw the movement as he stood above the eaglets' nest. He shrieked out and was joined by his mate who, till then, had remained hidden behind the ridge.

As the fox suddenly turned off toward the north, the crows, from force of habit because it was in their nature to distrust the red-coated one, started to fly after him. They called out derisively as they swooped down and drove the fox onward. The tree pipit followed, planing low to the ground and keeping in line with the gorse which would be a source of protection should the crows turn their attention on him.

By now, the entire moor was aware of the presence of Rashual and his mate, and of their pursuit of Tawny-eye. The stonechats were calling out up the whole length of the burn, and on Roineval itself, the eaglets were cheowping loudly for their parents.

The tree pipit, because he had startled the fox into movement, had at the same time distracted Rashual from his evil purpose. Now the whole of the wild life on the moor knew of the event, and before the crows could return, an enormous shadow swept over the rocks on Roineval as Groonah drifted upwind and hung poised, gazing down on the eyrie.

Meanwhile, Greesha had taken up the pursuit, not of Tawny-eye, but of Rashual and his mate. The crows saw his pinioned shape approaching. They went back over the moor toward Drynoch, shrieking out with fear. Their harsh voices could be heard long after Greesha had returned to his mate.

It seemed that though they were safe on their own nest, they could not subdue their hatred of the eagles, and must needs give vent to their rage by repeatedly calling out.

When at last they had screeched themselves into silence, and no further sound of their rage was carried on the breeze to Bealach Mor, life by the burn resumed its accustomed round. The stonechats flitted across the watercourse, moving lightly from boulder to boulder; the two crested tits sunned themselves on their favorite rock, and the tree pipit stood forlorn on the sprig of gorse watching them.

On Roineval itself, Groonah and Greesha stood motionless, keeping guard over the eaglets they had brought into the world on an eyrie that was over a thousand years old.

CHAPTER SIX

THE ROUTING OF THE HOODED CROWS

VERY LITTLE THE CHANGE ON ROINEVAL SINCE THE DAY — a thousand springs, or more perhaps — when the first eagles came flying out from the far islands of the north to nest on the crag where now Groonah and Greesha nested. Larger birds they were then maybe, cruel, savage and fearless. Not yet had they come under the persecution of man. Not for such regal birds in those far-off days of history in the Highlands, the gauntleted hand. One day they would be trained to pursue the wolves, then the rulers of the wild! All these things were to follow later. As yet man fought the unyielding wilderness for mastery. As yet there were no clans. Time passed and the changes came. The eagles retreated before the invading humans until at last, man grew ashamed.

During it all, family after family of eagles came to dwell on Roineval, the birds less fearless than their ancestors because they had grown to know man as the destroyer of their kind. Now was the time of Groonah and Greesha, sprung from those very first eagles who had come from out of the north to make their home on the misty Isle of Skye. Like their forebears they, too, were rearing their young on the ancient eyrie — Greeka and Altair. Greeka was the male eaglet; Altair was so named because on the night of her birth, Altair, the star of the Falconidae, had shone brightly over the crags of Roineval.

Their life span, longer by far than that of the man-god who now sparsely inhabited the Highlands, might see out a hundred years or more; and in a hundred years would grow their acceptance of knowledge until, wisest of the feathered tribe, they would know how best to harness their needs to the perpetual vagaries of Nature.

Many strange and beautiful things would they see from their mountain stronghold. For more mornings than man would ever know, they would witness the dawn invading their moorland territory. The world might well seem a very strange place in such a moment save to eyes long grown familiar to the event. No new thing for the eagles would be the age-old struggle of light against darkness, broken only by the quiet cheeping of birds on the very edge of the dawn. Down in the dark, across the loch, they would see the lights of the crofts gleam out as men and women stirred to the work of another day.

Maybe, up on the higher moor itself, the glen of the loch might be a darksome place — no wink of light visible — nothing save perhaps a phosphorus glow on the water as gradually the sky touched the rim of dawn gathering in the east.

Already part of the intricate pattern that made up the lives of the old birds, soon would these things be woven into the lives of Greeka and Altair. For them, as with their parents, there would be the shape of hills etched against the slow gathering van of the uprising sun, and, as had so often happened in the centuries that had gone, a curlew might shrill out, loud and clear, and it would be as though the young birds were glimpsing the rebirth of a new world. If there had been a heavy dew over night, they might well scent the rich earth stirring with the dawn, and hear the call of ewes and lambs.

In such an hour, there might be the broken murmur of the heather and whins in the sudden rising of the morning breezes, the whir of grouse passing over, kindling the desire to hunt.

Indeed, these things, and more, the eaglets would feel and know, living up there on the eyrie that had been the home of their kind throughout the centuries; even when they eventually went away to find a place of their own, still would they know the shape of hill and moor when the dawn came striding up from out of the east, and night slowly departed over the western ocean.

It was their heritage!

Yet, through it all, Roineval, up there on its ridge of moor, would remain much the same — the burn a little wider, maybe, with the years, the rocks a trifle more weather-shapen. As for the eagles that dwelled on the mountain, a more intimate knowing of the face of Nature, recurring memories of the moor in sunshine and rain, the burns in spate and perhaps no burns at all, with always another tomorrow beyond the rim of the world.

Groonah slept without movement throughout the long dark hours of the night following the crows' visit to the eyrie, not knowing that her own special tomorrow was approaching — the hour when she and Greesha must give battle to the scavengers from Drynoch in order to safeguard the lives of the eaglets.

Dawn was a long time coming on that fateful day in the lives of Rashual and his mate, but when at last the night was gone, it was a quiet, windless morning that had come to the mountains of the west. The sky was of an almost transparent blueness. As was their habit, the stonechats were out and about early, calling one to the other, and on a clump of heather, close to the eyrie, an inquisitive robin sat with head slightly tilted, completely unafraid of the huge bird brooding over her young. He twittered once or twice, and Groonah glanced up at him as if approving his efforts to charm the eaglets. For a long time the robin remained on his precarious perch, only flying away when Greesha came wheeling in with a grouse clutched in his talons.

Banking and gliding down silently, the eagle dropped the slain game bird on the larder rock, and then sat watching his mate feed the eaglets from the remains of the hare she had already prepared for their morning meal.

Just as Groonah commenced her toilet, Greesha uttered a warning cry.

The shepherd and his dog were once again coming up the glen!

Both birds watched his approach, noting in particular the direction pursued by the dog. Neither experienced undue anxiety at the shepherd's presence so early in the morning. He and his dog were a familiar sight, and the man had never troubled them. The reason for his benevolence, had they been able to comprehend it, was due to his receiving a grant each year from the Scottish Wild Birds Protection Society, and, apart from his sheep herding, it was one of his duties to see that the eagles were not molested and their nest robbed of its eggs or despoiled of its young.

The birds remained on the eyrie for some minutes before showing any sign of departing. Greesha made off first to take up a position of advantage on the opposite ridge of hills. Not long afterward, Groonah followed.

They had scarcely crossed the glen before the slinking shape of Tawny-eye appeared like a shadow around the lower flank of Roineval. The wily old fox had seen the shepherd moving up the track beside the burn, and, knowing that the eagles would leave the nest, was using the knowledge to his own advantage. Cringing low to the ground, he took to a narrow water gully, and hidden from sight, made his way upward in the direction of the eagles' larder.

The small robin watched him as he climbed, and kept glancing around to see if Groonah or her mate were near at hand. He whistled plaintively when he found that the old birds were nowhere visible. Flitting from rock to rock, he followed Tawny-eye's progress up the gully.

Fortunately for the fox, the gully cut deeply into the mountain, and he was thus able to reach the larder without being seen by either of the eagles on the lookout crags across the glen.

In a matter of seconds, he had reached the recess where the eaglets' food was stored. Picking up the plump grouse that Greesha had brought in less than an hour since, he crept back down the mountain and, reaching the open moor, made off with all speed for the cairn on Beinn Totaig, the grouse gripped tightly in his jaws. His heart beat joyfully as he ran. He had solved with ease the problem that had troubled him since he discovered that Biod was partial to wild fowl and grouse. His brief encounter with Groonah, on that rainy morning when she had swooped down out of the mist to catch a bird and take it back to the eyrie, had not been forgotten. As he saw it, for the present, at least, the eagles could do his hunting for him.

Only the sudden cheowping of the young birds in their nest reached his ears as he ran.

Meanwhile, the shepherd and his dog pressed on up the moor, turning westward when they reached the point where the burn branched off in the direction of the corrie.

It was a perfect morning. The sun was now well up behind hills that were sharp and perfectly massed on the horizon. The sky was flecked here and there with white, wispy
clouds that were almost motionless. In the east, the moon
that had been born in a welter of cloud was slowly dying,
becoming pale and wan as the sun grew in splendor over the
mountains. A lizard lay on a boulder by the burn, quiet and
patient, waiting for the sunlight to warm him. Near by, on
the close-cropped grass of the moor itself, rabbits were out
in fine style — in places, numbering as many as ten and
twelve. Far across the glen, a cuckoo was calling, strong and
clear; in the hollows, ewes silently grazing ceased for a second or two to feed their ever-hungry lambs.

Way over, the shepherd was singing.

> *"Up in th' mornin's no for me,*
> *Up in th' mornin' early.*
> *When a' th' hills are covered wi' snow,*
> *I'm sure it's winter fairly!"*

Then because it wasn't winter, but spring, he began to
sing another tune.

> *"I've heard them liltin' at our ewe-milkin',*
> *Lasses a-liltin' before th' dawn o' day.*
> *But now they are moanin' on ilka green loanin',*
> *The flowers o' th' forest are a' wede away!"*

Scotland, in spring, was a grand place surely. No better
could be found the whole world over. Yet, in that grand

world that was so bright with sunshine and song, way over above Drynoch, Rashual, the hooded crow, was summoning others of his tribe against the eagles on Roineval.

He little knew that on her lookout post way across the glen, Groonah's gaze was centred on the eyrie, and her far-seeing eye could penetrate the moor around Drynoch — the home of the hoodie crows!

She was still watching intently when the shepherd and his dog had vanished over the western hills. Then quietly, she flew back across the glen to nestle her young while Gree-sha set off on his hunting.

The gathering of the crows had come about soon after daybreak. Rashual and his quarrelsome mate had been quartering the moor above the bridge near Braigh Aluinn when others of his family put in an appearance. Soon afterward, Rashual's mate discovered the carcass of a ram which had fallen into the burn and now, since the water was running low, was left exposed on an immense slab of rock. She gave a harsh croak of pleasure, and within a few minutes, some dozen or more hooded crows were bickering and fighting over the creature's remains.

Long before they were satisfied, the carcass lay stripped, and the crows were soon looking for something else to satisfy their craving for excitement.

Nature herself must have taken a special interest in their affairs that morning by sending over their territory the very old buzzard, Merroo. The bird possessed none of the fine attributes of his younger brethren. He had grown lean and scraggy since he had ceased to be agile in hunting. More important, he was given to long periods of inactivity, being a very lonely bird since losing his mate some three springs before.

Thus Nature, in providing him as prey for the marauding crows, was bringing to an end a life that had lost its savor.

The black scavengers of the wild saw Merroo the instant he flew laboriously over Braigh Aluinn. Almost blind with age, the buzzard was unaware of his attackers until Rashual swept down upon him. A short cry like that of a kitten in distress came from the stricken bird as the crow struck him, and Merroo, the buzzard of Glen Drynoch, was dead before his body hit the ground.

Then was born the moment when Rashual's cunning brain devised the scheme of attack on the eagles of Roineval and the seizure of the eaglets. No sooner had his brethren torn to pieces the body of Merroo than Rashual summoned them with a call and led them off across the moor.

Groonah, having tidied up the eyrie by carrying off the refuse, was decorating the nest with some fresh sprigs of heather when suddenly the crows came over the ridge of the mountain in a solid mass. She swung off the eyrie to face them and was less than a hundred feet up when Rashual went in to the attack. Almost at once, the eagle found herself being mobbed by the excited crows.

She tried to elude them in an effort to regain the eyrie and so better protect herself and her young; but the crows had surrounded her. Banking quickly, she managed to avoid the crows' repeated thrusts at her. She was, however, at a disadvantage. She was out of the wind currents and her flight was labored.

Then from way up, she heard a call. Greesha was coming to her assistance!

Returning to the nest from a hunting expedition in the Trotternish, he was approaching the height of Beinn Totaig when he saw the crows swoop over the ridge of Roineval. He immediately released his grip on the rabbit he was bringing in, and banking, soared upward to over a thousand feet. He then took a pitch directly over the scene of the conflict, and hovered for a moment, sending out his warning call to Groonah. As he held his position in the wind currents, he saw his mate break away from her attackers, and with them close behind her, succeed in reaching an altitude of some four hundred feet. He knew then that she had understood his call, and was making way for his opening thrust.

Greesha brought his huge pinions close to his body, and began a most spectacular fall earthward. Like a lightning flash he came — swifter and ever swifter, cleaving the air with a wild strumming of the wind in his tail feathers.

Down he came, heading straight for the attacking crows. Then he was on them, and as he passed through their now serried ranks, out came one foot, the talons striking as a falcon strikes, severing the head from the body of Rashual himself.

Uttering loud cries of alarm, the crows scattered for an instant, then as Greesha flattened out to soar once again, they turned and renewed their attack, this time on him.

Groonah now rose to an immense height, taking much the same pitch as had her mate. Then, like him, down she came in a stoop that, while less spectacular, was yet one of wild savagery. Through the ranks of the battling crows she went, but not striking at them as Greesha had done. As she opened her pinions to check the fall, two of the invaders were knocked out of the air and killed by the sheer impetus of the sudden spreading of those powerful wings.

The crows were now swayed by a common impulse of fear. They tried to mass together for protection, but Greesha, having been freed from their attention by Groonah's offensive action, had once more cut a perfect arc in the sky and taken his pitch for another deadly assault.

Both eagles were now working together as though by instinct. Groonah had swept around in a wide circle, driving the crows even closer together. Then again her mate came hurtling down, more formidable than ever. Right into the very midst of the crows did he go, and once more did he strike with his talons after the manner of a falcon, and yet another of his enemies fell on to the moor, its head severed as if by a razor blade.

That was the end of the battle. The crows separated, and

tried to make off as quickly as possible, with the eagles harrying them all the way to Drynoch.

On the nest, Greeka and Altair were cheowping noisily, their wild blood exultant. The hoodie crows had been completely defeated, and would never again attempt to ravish the eyrie on Roineval.

That night, under the quiet stars and quieter moon, the moor was silent as if the conflict of the day had never been. Only the slow-moving figure of a fox stalked abroad, searching for the bodies of the crows which he carried, with haste, up to the cairn on Beinn Totaig. In Loch Vidigill, the moon, which had been born in a tumult of storm clouds, shone white and clear. Then Kehonka, a wild goose from the north, went flying over. A snipe sounded soft and low. Soon afterward, a brace of duck took off from amongst the reeds and sailed away into the western night — two lonely shapes winging after the more lonely shape of Kehonka who was bound on a far journey.

Then again, the night sank down in peace to brood, and the silent steps of darkness trod toward the edge of a new day.

CHAPTER SEVEN

THE SAGA OF TAWNY-EYE

The Second and Final Phase

THERE WAS NO SIGN OF A BREAK IN THE WEATHER. THE spring days continued warm and bright — almost like summer come before its time. Sheep lay panting in the haughs of the moor; grouse squatted hidden in the shadows of the outcrops. Ofttimes, there was heard over the mountain ridges a hillbird's cry — wild, lamenting; it would go up into the silence only to die away as a winged shadow came sweeping up the glen to come to rest on Roineval.

Then for an hour, perhaps longer, a fierce-eyed bird would sit staring out across the small corrie. The only sound would be the low, musical laugh of the burn; and the bird would see the clouds wandering and passing out over the tableland of the Trotternish Mountains, and the hills, with the shadows dropping down on them, would seem full of movement, softened by distance, and less formidable in the bright springtime light. Although these were the days of rebirth, they were days of peace and rare beauty, save for one creature who dwelt on Bealach Mor.

That was Tawny-eye! For him, they were days of stress and a queer foreboding. Even in his hunting and stealing, he was aware of some strange fate hanging over him. Moreover, he felt powerless to break its spell.

Up on Beinn Totaig, under the small pile of stones, lay Biod; her head and shoulders were alive; the rest of her was completely dead! Her tongue was swollen and black, the only moisture that had touched it these many days having come from the game Tawny-eye brought, and which she bit into but could not eat. Her eyes alone disclosed that life still struggled for existence in her useless body; they reflected more often than not the one creature who refused to desert her in this, the hour of her great tribulation.

Like the eagles, always within easy range of the eyrie on Roineval, Tawny-eye was never far from the lair under the cairn on Beinn Totaig.

He spent many long hours lying close to the entrance, staring in at Biod who seemed never to sleep, but just looked at him and the downward sweep of the hill beyond. Heaped up about her were the decaying carcasses of rabbits and hare, and, the most recent of Tawny-eye's acquisitions, the headless bodies of two hooded crows.

Biod was no longer conscious of hunger — only the discomfort of a great thirst. The heat of the last few days had worsened her condition, and with the fatalistic instinct of the wild, she knew that soon now the great darkness would engulf her, and free Tawny-eye of his self-imposed bondage.

In some vague way, the old dog fox possessed this same knowledge. Yet, unlike Biod, because he was strong and could move at will up and down the moor, he refused to accept the clear indications of defeat.

When suddenly overtaken by sleep, and he lay stretched out before the entrance to the lair, it seemed that life had become less troublesome, that he and the vixen were running together under the cloudless sky, beneath the bright stars of a spring night.

Together they would visit the tarn at the foot of Beinn Totaig, and Biod's tongue would no longer be swollen and black between her jaws, but exactly like his — eager to lap; and her legs, those useless sticks would be, like his, firm and swift in movement, quick in leaping, well able to carry her body with ease to the places he was anxious to lead her.

Only when he awakened and saw Biod gravely watching him did he know and acknowledge the truth.

Biod, he sensed, had been living those dreams with him. Her eyes, on the occasions of his awakening, had been eloquent with all the things that, for a space, had taken her away with him across the wide, breeze-haunted sweep of Bealach Mor.

On the third morning following the routing of the hoodie crows by the eagles of Roineval, Tawny-eye made slow progress down toward the Vidigill tarn. He was exceedingly low in spirits. The air of bravado had at last deserted him. His brush was no longer the gay banner of his independence. He knew that on this — the morning of the red sun — something vital was happening under the pile of stones on Beinn Totaig. Biod's eyes had warned him. Moreover, he sensed, too, that somehow the night that would come up with its myriad stars would be different.

What he did not sense was that neither he nor Biod would be there — on Bealach Mor — to see the new night with its old, seemingly changeless stars.

Tawny-eye found the tarn deserted when he reached it. The wild duck that were usually hiding in the reeds, when the old fox came down to drink, were gone. Tawny-eye's stealth in stalking had not passed unnoticed. The tarn was just a deep, dark pool, the water unruffled, reflecting only the sun which, having risen a burnished red, had not changed as the morning hours sped on toward high noon.

The fox stood for quite a while, his muzzle wet from his recent drinking.

At last, as if he had finally made an important decision, Tawny-eye loped back up the hill, pausing uncertainly at the cairn, fully aware that Biod still gazed out of the entrance. This time, however, her eyes were not beholding him, but only the fall of the slope toward the tarn where was water — water which might bring movement to her limbs and a renewed life to the flame that was flickering low, so soon now to be extinguished.

Suddenly Tawny-eye had gone from the scene, making

off southeast in the direction of the small corrie guarding Roineval and the crags of the eagles' eyrie.

Approaching the mountain ridge by way of the gap between the two burns, he halted for a moment, flairing the air currents. He then moved off due east, finally ascending Roineval from the Drynoch side. This was purely a matter of strategy on his part, for he was able to make use of the rough, boulder-strewn slope to advantage, and by keeping close to the rocks was, for most of the ascent, completely under cover. As he came up toward the summit ridge, he heard the eaglets moving about restlessly, and sensed by their bickering that the old birds were away from the nest.

Once again he paused, staring about him apprehensively. Finding that neither Groonah nor Greesha were visible, he went straight to the larder. There was another plump grouse in the rock acclivity, and catching it up in his jaws, he made off immediately. As on the other occasions when he had raided the eyrie, he kept well to the depression of an old watercourse on his way back to Beinn Totaig.

Biod must have heard the swift movement of his feet when at last he came up to the cairn. He heard her whine. With brush well raised, he crept up to the entrance of the lair and deposited the bird between her outstretched paws.

The vixen whined once again. Tawny-eye took it to mean that she was pleased with the grouse he had brought. Had he not experienced a sudden wave of excitement at the sound of her voice, he might have known the reason for her whine.

Biod was frightened — more than she had ever been since that first great fear that had told her she would never move again from the lair.

Even as her ears registered the quick patter of Tawny-eye's feet approaching the cairn, so did she know that the great darkness she dreaded was about to engulf her. She gave another anxious whine as Tawny-eye dropped the body of the grouse within reach of her jaws.

Then it was all over. The last thing she saw was the old dog fox silhouetted against the sky, his brush slowly lowering. Then the light went from her eyes. She had seen Tawny-eye for the last time. Yet, no movement came from her as life departed. She continued to lie where she had lain for so many long days — a stark image whose eyes had so quickly become little more than dead stones in her head.

As the fox backed away from the entrance to the lair, he continued to look at her. Biod seemed the same, yet somehow different! He was puzzled and a little disconcerted.

He lay quietly watching her. After a time he dozed, while the red sun slipped down the sky toward the west and the eastern slope of the cairn became dark with heavy shadows. Since Tawny-eye fell into his doze, the eagles had passed twice over the humped shape of Beinn Totaig. On the third occasion when they winged their way leisurely over the summit toward the Trotternish range, Tawny-eye suddenly roused himself and stared into the lair. The red light from the sun spilled into the entrance and upon the figure of Biod.

Tawny-eye jumped to his feet, his ears aslant on his skull. A goosander, fresh come to the tarn, cried out in a strident voice; a reed bunting gave a plaintive answer.

The fox did not hear them. His head had dropped between his shoulders as he continued to gaze into the lair. He seemed to see the vixen more clearly than he had ever seen her before.

It was Biod no longer. During his sleep she had changed. She still looked out on to the moor, now strangely softened in the late afternoon light; but Tawny-eye knew that she did not see him, nor the moor, nor the red sun glimmering behind the haze above the Trotternish Mountains.

Quickly, as if in fear, he glanced over his shoulder. He took in at a glance what she had seen so long in her captivity — the downward sweep of the hill and the western sky which, that afternoon, was of a dull, coppery color.

Again the goosander cried out, the sound following Tawny-eye as he turned and loped rapidly down the hill in the direction of that stretch of moorland which was no longer a part of the vixen's world.

Fear lent speed to Tawny-eye's feet. At first, he sped almost blindly from the scene, stumbling where the ground was broken by boulders and steep ledges. Then, as if having got into his stride, he ran swift and sure — straight toward Roineval and the eyrie where the eaglets were cheowping for their parents.

The shadow of his own destiny followed him, for Groonah, coming in from the Trotternish tableland, swung headlong into the breeze and glided effortlessly over the moor.

Tawny-eye forgot the need for caution and seemed completely unaware that the young birds were calling out a greeting to either Greesha or Groonah.

Running an almost straight line, he came down off the hill, no longer seeking out the old watercourse — his red shape conspicuous against the gray-green of the cotton grass and heather. Reaching the small corrie, he waded across the burn at a point where boulders broke the flow of the water.

He was moving mechanically, going through an old and familiar routine that had become a habit difficult to break.

While it was an unnamable fear that had driven him from the cairn, habit brought him down off the hill and along the trail to the corrie at the foot of Roineval. His sense of strategy had deserted him. He had forgotten that he had already been to the eyrie once that day and robbed the eagles' larder. Even the memory of Biod as he had seen her a short time before was becoming dim in his mind. All he knew was that he was scrambling up the crags of the mountain ridge, that up on them — in an acclivity — was an abundance of food.

Making no pause when he came to an overhang of rock, he pressed on, seemingly without regard for life and limb. More than ever did he seem like a creature acting without reason, moving as if directed by some obscure impulse that he could not resist.

The route he had taken brought him within a few feet of the nest itself. Bunched together as if for protection, the young eaglets were watching him, both silent now that danger threatened them. Hovering high over the crags was Groonah herself.

It seemed that in that moment there was a strained silence resting over the moor. A cloud brushed like gauze across the face of the westering sun.

Tawny-eye half crouched, his muscles taut to leap on to the crag above him. The same instant saw the eaglets fluff out their downy feathers, Altair, bristling with rage and raising one leg in readiness to strike should the fox invade the nest.

With a twisted snarl on his mask, the fox made the spring upward in the direction of the larder — appeared to hang stationary for a second as his forepaws went out to grapple with the rock . . .

It was then as the gauzelike cloud passed from the face of the sun that Groonah struck! Her huge shape swept down, talons extended. The sudden opening of her wide pinions hid for a moment the figure of the fox.

Then it came — a sharp, rising note of anguish as the eagle's talons sank into his body. Before the cry had died away, Groonah released her merciless grip, and the torn body of her victim fell with a thud on to the rocks below.

There had been no struggle from Tawny-eye. He had been taken entirely by surprise. The eagle's grip had pierced his heart and he was dead before his paws had found foothold on the crag he had sought to reach.

So died Tawny-eye, the vagabond fox of Bealach Mor!

A mass of cumulus cloud lay heavy in the west and the red-glowing sun wheeled down behind the hills to become lost in the Hebridean sea. Quietly then, came an overwhelming sense of loneliness to the moor, a sense of things once seen and never glimpsed again. All creatures of the wild were part of that immense loneliness — all no different than Tawny-eye — mere motes in the speeding of time which knew neither man nor animal, and was of itself omnipotent!

CHAPTER EIGHT

WHEN THE EAGLE STIRRETH HER WINGS

SPRING HAD MANY WEEKS SINCE GONE THE WAY OF PREVIOUS seasons, and June was already advancing on to midsummer. Gone now the look of winter on the hills. Instead, there was the blink of haze on the peaks, and the purple glow of heather where the slopes ran down to the burns. The blow of the wind from off the braes would ofttimes be soft and with no bite in it at all, and certainly no memory of the days when it came from off the sea behind the sting of rain and ragged, drifting cloud.

On the moors, sheepherders were hard at work, shearing their younger ewes and marking their late-born lambs, while overhead, swallows turned in swift and dazzling flight. Most all the birds of that year's brood had left their nests and were out in the world, most all, save the young reared by the largest of them — the eagles! In many eyries, eaglets still called loudly for food, and their parents were as busy as when the young had first been hatched. Not so, however, on Roineval. The old birds had served the eaglets well, and of all the fledglings who had grown to near maturity, there were none in the whole of the Western Isles like Altair and Greeka. It was clear that before the month of June had passed, they would be out of the nest — perhaps never to return. Maybe, for another month or so, they would remain in the vicinity of Bealach Mor, but never more would they be held to one place.

As the long days of summer passed toward the heel of the month, the young birds often gave violent displays of activity, particularly on those occasions when either Groonah or her mate swung in low over the ridge with fresh food.

One morning, near to midday, Greesha, returning unexpectedly to the nest, found the eaglets sunning themselves on the lip of the plateau. He immediately made off, returning a few minutes later with his mate.

Yet, despite these infrequent excursions away from the nest, it soon became clear to the old birds that for the present, at least, neither Altair nor Greeka were prepared to wander too far from the place where they had been born. They were, however, constantly testing their wings by flapping them, thus forcing out the last of the downy feathers that still clung to their bodies. Both had a habit of wandering along the ridge, but dusk always found them back at the nest watching anxiously for the return of the old birds.

Late one afternoon when Greeka and Altair were sitting on the ridge staring away over the moor, a bird, larger than either of their parents, came gliding low up the glen. They stood up and cheowped loudly. The bird banked, swooped upward with apparent ease and glided to the ridge.

It was Vigur, the great sea eagle, from Dranga Jokull many miles north in Iceland. A rare visitor to the Highlands of Scotland, his ancestors had yet come from Skye, and often, when the mating season was past, he came riding down with the wind to those hunting grounds his clan had deserted through persecution, and there were occasions — as now — when he penetrated down the coast of Skye, but never proceeding beyond to the lower isles.

He alighted on a crag at the eastern edge of the ridge and watched the eaglets. They continued to cheowp, Altair making a great fuss as she spread her pinions.

Vigur was reminded of his own offspring in the snowy wastes of Dranga Jokull. Hardy birds they were to be sure, but not so far advanced as these two who seemed annoyed at his presence.

As they continued to fuss, expanding their feathers so that he could see clearly the white tail band of their infancy, Vigur supposed them to be of his own race, for the white tail feathers was the only distinguishing mark, apart from size, that characterized the Sea Eagle from his near relative the Golden Eagle.

He was vastly intrigued by the young birds' antics, and gave a yelping cry of greeting that might well have come from either Greesha or Groonah. Then suddenly shaking himself, he flew off the crag and skirted the ridge, keeping close to the rocks as if searching the ledges for a rabbit or other likely game. In a matter of seconds he had seen a lizard, and keeling over, swooped down, then swerved upward, the creature wriggling in his talons. Straight over the young birds he went, dropping the lizard within reach of their feet.

In a moment, both eaglets were quarreling for possession of this new type of food that Vigur had supplied, and as the sea eagle landed once again on the crag, their cries attracted the attention of Greesha and Groonah who were quartering the slopes of Beinn Totaig. They thrust up immediately above the summit of the mountain, wheeled quickly, and then came gliding across the moor.

Vigur saw them approaching at great speed, and having no desire to quarrel with such close relatives as the golden eagles, he launched himself from the crag and started to soar. The initial advantage was with Greesha and his mate, for they were already on the wing and coming straight at Vigur like bronze thunderbolts.

The sea eagle, however, was spiraling rapidly, having got into a keen run of air. He was perfectly balanced, his pinions stretched to their fullest extent as if searching out every drift of wind to aid him in his flight.

Groonah went up after him while Greesha swept in low over Roineval to see how the young birds were behaving. Both were in no way alarmed. Greeka, having given up his struggle for the lizard, was showing the greatest interest in the sudden departure of the sea eagle.

The appearance of the huge bird from the north had roused in him a rare sense of excitement. As he watched Vigur soaring away up into the blue, pursued by his mother, Greeka little guessed that he was to see him again, and at a time when the sea eagle's prowess in hunting was to enable the younger bird to survive a winter of famine.

Meanwhile, Vigur was being harried by Groonah, and Greesha was also swooping up to lend her assistance.

Vigur, like all of his clan, was not in the least perturbed, and each time Groonah swept up under his tail feathers, he just keeled over and glided out of reach with an ease the golden eagle herself would have found difficult to match for sheer mastery of the air. Then, as if to confuse both Groonah and Greesha, and mock them in their efforts to harry the sea eagle, a skein of wild gray geese came flying up from the Vidigill Tarn, spread out in V formation and heading for the coast.

Instantly Vigur made a sudden turn, then thrust up at an amazing speed that left the two golden eagles still spiraling around below.

At the very moment that Greesha and his mate soared up to reach him, the sea eagle went into a stoop. He made straight for the leader of the geese, legs thrust out and talons glinting like knives in the sun. He struck with a resounding thud at the bird he had selected, and the goose was dead, his loosened feathers streaming away behind him as Vigur, with a beat of his pinions, turned due north and headed for the Trotternish Mountains.

So sudden and unexpected was the attack that the sea eagle was well away before either Greesha or Groonah realized that he had gone.

With his abrupt departure from the scene, all thought of him went, too, and the two eagles from Roineval also started a combined assault on the geese which, though their leader had met with a sudden end, had not broken formation, but continued on their journey seaward.

Two more geese met the same abrupt end that had over-taken their leader, and were carried back to the larder on Roineval, while over on the Trotternish tableland, Vigur feasted alone until only a few bones and feathers remained of his kill.

Less than an hour later, he was on the wing again and soon encircling the Isle of Rona where seals lay basking in the sun. Even there — in the bay of the seals — he was lucky in his hunting, for a salmon broke surface off shore, and as it leaped a crested breaker, Vigur swooped. The large, eight-pound fish was held in relentless talons that slew him as surely as they had slain the wild gray goose.

By sundown, however, the sea eagle had gone, heading back over the miles of ocean to his home in the far-off moun-tains of Dranga Jokull. The Bay of Seals was quiet and peaceful, the outward swinging tides little more than a ripple along the island coast.

Way over on Skye, above the volcanic crags of Roineval, Greesha and Groonah thrust up at each other in tireless play, while in the nest, two sleepy eaglets stared away across the moor, all events of the day forgotten in the sluggishness that followed a heavy meal.

West of Beinn Totaig, in a mossy hollow, a few gray feathers, blood-stained, quivered in the evening breeze. They were the only evidence that a great bird from the snowy wastes of Iceland had visited for a while the island home that had once cradled his ancestors.

An hour later, it was night once again on Bealach Mor!

The days grew hotter as the month slipped by. Grand weather it was for summer, sure enough, but unusual for Skye where most days of the year there was rain. Down on the crofting lands, the earth was soft with the crops steadily ripening, so different from a month or so back when the whole of the island was happed in driving rain, and the mountains steeped in mist.

Then soon after dawn one morning, there was a flying and calling of rooks from Carbost, and there, surely, was rain drumming down out of the sunlit sky and casting a veil over the Trotternish glen. Sheep quickly bunched together under the outcrops of rock, and soon the burns were rising with a merry note.

Not for long though, the summer rain. In no time, it was

drifting seaward in looping whorls that scarcely touched the summits of the hills. Nevertheless, brief though it was, it had freshened the earth, and snipe were sounding over the moors.

Because of the freshness of the air that morning, Groonah started clearing out the larder and, not long afterward, was disposing of all the old bones that littered the nest.

Her task completed, she stood for a while on the summit ridge, and as the rain went drifting off, she felt an urge to follow it. The young birds were safe on the plateau, and she made off, flying swiftly away in the direction of the Trotternish tableland where she knew Greesha to be.

These were the days when both Greeka and Altair were more often out of the nest than in it. Although they had attempted nothing in the way of actual flight, they did make good use of their wings to aid them to reach the plateau. Occasionally, Groonah would visit them and refuse to offer them food until she had given them a lesson in flying.

To encourage them to follow her, her usual practice was to bring in a hare which she carried to an exposed crag where they could see it. She then made short flights from boulder to boulder, always moving in the direction of the pinnacle.

Neither Greeka nor Altair displayed much interest in her antics, both knowing that sooner or later she would tire of her efforts, and retrieving the hare leave it for them to eat or quarrel over as they wished.

In many respects, Groonah was a tolerant mother, but

from long experience, she understood the laziness so often manifest in young birds. She knew, as well as they did, that when the time came, they would fly easily enough. Although she liked to encourage them to use their wings, whether they did so early or late made no difference to the ultimate outcome. Flying to them would be an instinctive reaction, as indeed it was to all birds of prey, for by it they hunted and had their being.

Notwithstanding, she still continued to encourage them whenever she returned from a hunting expedition and found them absent from the nest and whiling away the hours on the plateau.

The fact that they were now well able to skin their own food, and did it quite efficiently, gave her longer periods away from them, and in this, too, she was inherently teaching them some of the most important principles of life — to be patient and watch, thereby making good use of their eyes.

In this, they were already adept. Scarcely a thing happened in the vicinity of the plateau but that they were aware of it. For them, as with the old birds, the shape of every boulder, and the run and twist of the burn through the small corrie, were things to be regarded and studied as part of the great hunting grounds they must one day frequent.

Altair was the first to bestir herself into flying, never making the attempt until Groonah had gone off with Greesha. When she was sure that the old birds were no longer near by, with a wild flapping of wings she made short flights across the plateau, making for those same boulders her mother was in the habit of using.

Greeka soon followed her example, and although neither of the birds rose more than a few feet off the ground, they were yet unknowingly instructing themselves in the main rudiments of flying.

Then an event of importance happened in the lives of the young birds. Altair made her first kill!

It took place a week or so after Vigur's sudden arrival and equally sudden departure. Altair was quickened into movement by the appearance of a stoat making his way along the watercourse at the foot of one of the outcrops.

For over an hour that morning, Altair had been sunning herself in a particularly warm hollow when the creature put in an appearance. To her, as she looked and bristled, he seemed little more than an unusually outsize member of the lizard family to whom she had already been agreeably introduced by the sea eagle.

The feathers on her neck stood out with excitement as she kept close watch on the stoat's progress. All the primitive instincts of her kind were roused. From the very moment that the stoat attracted her attention, she had, subconsciously, bridged the gap between passiveness and the desire to hunt.

Greeka was completely unaware of the events that were unfolding in the lives of them both. He was sitting some distance away with his back to the sun, looking out over the corrie and the thin trickle of the burn.

Altair tensed herself to make her first attack. There was not the slightest sign of ill-considered haste in her actions. The very stiffening of her pinions indicated absolute control, tempered with a deep-seated knowledge that could only have come from those who were her parents.

As it was, the stoat himself was fully aware that he was under observation, but being old and full of wisdom, he had confidence in his ability to outwit the eagle, knowing her to be young and inexperienced.

In this lay the fatal error that was to cost him his life. As he made a sudden dart forward at the remains of a rabbit left by the young birds, so did Altair take instinctively to flight. No wild fluttering of pinions this time, just a swift glide across the plateau that took the stoat by surprise.

With no outcrop now to protect his flank, he reared up, his feet striking at the air. He saw the shape of the eagle swoop over him, and as he turned to meet the bird face to face, Altair, with an adroit turn, had swung about again.

The harassed stoat realized too late that he had misjudged the flying powers of the young bird. In an effort to gain an advantage over his attacker, he rolled sinuously to one side, making an upward snap at a pinion that suddenly enwrapped him. Wriggling free, he essayed a swift dart back to the security of the crag; but too late — Altair had cut off his line of retreat, and before he could remedy his desperate position, she had struck with her talons.

One broken hiss escaped from the stricken creature as he

died. Then Altair sat quietly with the body quivering in her talons while Greeka, attracted by the sudden flight of his sister, half flew and half hopped to where she sat.

She would not let him approach too close. The kill she had made was hers by right of claw, and even when the old birds swung in over the ridge, she refused to leave the body of the stoat, but tore it into small pieces which she devoured with an arrogant air.

CHAPTER NINE

SWIFTER THAN THE EAGLE

ALTAIR WAS NEARING THE HOUR OF HER DEPARTURE FROM
the eyrie on Roineval. For days now there had been peewits
crying across the Drynoch heuchs, and snipe drumming in
the neighborhood of the Vidigill Tarn. There was a recurring
restlessness about these sounds; moreover, they were somehow insistent that all watchers of the wild should listen and
learn, for the lesson they had to tell was of life outside the
confines of Roineval.

The young eagle often frequented one of the loftiest
crags on the volcanic ridge as her perch, and from such an
important height, she was able to hear also other more distant sounds, some coming from as far off as the Meadale
Glen and Loch Harport. Down there, above the loch, gulls
seemed always to be calling as they swooped over the water;
and there was the cry of crows above the turrets of Talisker.

Another thing about that lofty eminence on Roineval
intrigued Altair. Below it, the green and purple moors were
smoothed away toward remote horizons, and little burns
glinted in the morning light.

Frowning, however, over them all were the giant peaks of the Cuillins, and eastward, the serrated shape of the mountain Blaven, with the medieval ridge of Clach Glas seeming like a back cloth of cardboard joining the seaward escarpment with the hooked peak of Garbh-bheinn that lay well back toward Strath Mor and the Glen of the Red Deer.

Altair was inclined to view the distant ramparts of the Cuillins with disdain; for her, the Trotternish range with a glimpse of the sea beyond! She sat for many hours of the day staring into that westward vista of blue sky and blue sea, with the vast tableland of mountain seeming, from Roineval, like the last of the world with nothing beyond but the great, uncharted flight ways of the Falconidae.

Had the shepherd, who so often came up the moor to tend his sheep, glimpsed her then as she sat staring away off into those far horizons, he would have declared that she would fly higher and farther than any other bird of her race.

Her very bearing on that rock pinnacle was a symbol of the power that the Great Spirit of the Wild had given to those of the Eagle tribe!

The week that saw the departure of the snipe from the Vidigill Tarn and witnessed the flight of the peewits across the Drynoch heuchs to Glen Sligachan was also a week of momentous importance in the destinies of the eagles on Roineval. On the very hour that Greeka called out loudly to the old birds as they flew off toward the Trotternish tableland, so did Altair suddenly know that if she wished, she too could quarter that distant mountain range. The power of flight was strong in her pinions!

Thus on that special day of days, and on that very hour when Greeka repeatedly called out to the old birds, to Altair had come a vision far removed from her present surroundings. The wind had brought it to her. As it aided the old birds in their flight toward the Trotternish tableland, so did it bring to Altair the sensation of suppressed power — power in those pinions she kept spreading in luxurious enjoyment. There were moments when a gust half lifted her as it got beneath her wings.

The vision, therefore, that came to Altair was the age-old vision of every member of the Falconidae — the vision of soundless flight in the wide arc of the sky.

Yet, despite the feeling of buoyancy she experienced, and the knowledge that she could, without effort, take to wing any hour she chose, she still delayed launching off.

When the wind had dropped a little of its wildness, and the old birds had gone, and Greeka sat staring upward in silence on the ledge he had made his own, Altair remained motionless on her pinnacle, her head set in the direction of the distant sea. Her pinions were still partially splayed like a royal garment set out for the approbation of Nature — the mother of all living creatures!

Her moment was gathering about her in a great spinning cycle of time; and it was time stretched out in one eternal atom of concentrated power and ecstasy. Unblinking and unmoving though she was on that wind-swept crag above Roineval, she was nevertheless aware of all that moment would give her. She did not need the old birds now to tell her what she already knew. Neither did she require the food they still brought. Those tireless talons of hers, forever opening and closing, conveyed, as nothing else could, the meaning of their existence which was closely allied to flight itself.

Imperishable aeons of timeless living, caught up and gathered in a fine-spun bloodstream of innumerable generations of eagles, throbbed and burned in her very heart and veins. Like all other creatures of the wild, she knew instinctively what Nature itself knew. She sensed her whole destiny lay in flight, but her knowledge came from events of the past and not of the immediate present. What had never existed in her bloodstream could not exist in Altair as a living organism of the wild!

On that special morning on the misty Isle of Skye, perhaps Nature, her guardian, knew of the thing that was already taking shape way out in space where time and event were brought into being. Perhaps the sky and the wind knew — perhaps, too, the quietly returning sea sweeping around Idrigill Point and up into Loch Bracadale knew. Maybe, at that very hour were gathering the tidal forces that, within a few dawns, would result in an almost tideless sea flowing into the loch — a sea so still that at sunset, one bright star would shine in it as serenely as in a mirror: but Altair, born of Groonah and Greesha on an eyrie on Roineval, did not know!

Her wisdom was assuredly only the wisdom of the past and not of the future. For swifter than the eagle in flight would it come on her — the thing she did not know as she sat spreading her wings and preening herself on that isolated crag that overlooked her birthplace.

For three days longer, Altair sat on the crag, while her approaching moment grew vast and omnipotent around her. The old birds had become almost strangers, and it was only due to increasing hunger that she partook of some of the food they brought in.

As for Greeka, he too was conscious that soon he would be taking to the air, and save for infrequent intervals on the plateau, most of his time was spent on the ledge looking out on the expanse of Bealach Mor. Unlike his sister, he sat staring away to the distant ramparts of the Black Cuillins. When the wind spoke to him, it brought a vision different from Altair's. While there was the suggestion of early flight in its promptings, its main theme was always of the wild corries of Clach Glas and the Blaven ridge where was a solitude and silence greater than any he had experienced on Bealach Mor.

Thus while Greeka sat and stared southward, and Altair luxuriously spread her pinions as if to strengthen them for the flight she soon would make, the weather continued fine

and unbroken, although a change was indicated by the varying wind currents that came in from the western sea. The
burns were running low; the tarns quiet and unruffled. A
few birds of the common sandpiper species had invaded the
silent little loch on the northwestern slopes of Beinn Totaig
where not so long ago the snipe had been, and their shrill
voices disturbed the heights of the mountain where, under
a pile of stones, a vixen, long dead, stared away across the
downward slope of the hill as if at eternity itself.

Altair's hour came to her when down over the moor a
curlew called out shrill and clear. She raised her head and
listened as once, on a stormy night when she was a nestling,
her mother had listened to the crying of a sheep about to die.

Again the curlew fluted out, the note rising and falling
like the faint piping of a braw Hieland man long since gone
across the dark water of the loch at World's End, and now
trying in vain to pipe his way back to the sunset land of
mountain and burn.

Then another sound came up out of the moor to tell her of
the unknown life that existed beyond the foothills of Roineval. This time it was an otter whistling in the burn where
the water gathered in a rock basin for a stupendous run over
a fall. Other less-penetrating sounds told of cubs not a great
distance off.

There was a keen ripple of breeze coming off the distant
Trotternish heights, and over the lower reaches of the burn,
swallows were flying low — a sign of the coming change in

the weather. The curlew was still fluting down across the moor, while far up, high over Beinn Totaig, a falcon hung poised — a palpitating speck in the blue of the sky.

Altair, on her rock pinnacle, listened and watched, her wings fully spread and her knifelike talons making scrabbling movements among the loose boulders.

Greeka, as usual, was squatting on his ledge contemplating the vast domain that would soon be his to conquer. His hour, unlike that of Altair, was not yet come, thus he was able to sit in idle contemplation of the savage peaks that were slowly growing crimson as the westering sun began to go sharply down the uncharted flight ways of the sky.

The wind was coming in a little more strongly, veering around and blowing from the south. It seemed to have many voices that evening — voices that spoke loudly and long to Altair as she sat in readiness on her mountain crag.

Even as Tawny-eye, the vagabond fox, had been influenced by the wind on that morning which was the beginning of his saga of self-sacrifice, so now was Altair — the Golden Eagle — similarly influenced. She puffed out her feathers with impatience, and her talons scrabbled once more among the boulders. The wind appeared to be sweeping over the plateau in varying ripples, some strong, some scarcely more than a whispering breath of air.

The sun was sinking faster now, so it seemed, burning above the hills in deepening tones of orange. Rivers of light moved along the rim of the Trotternish range; the western sea beyond was like a golden mirror, no inward surge of tide, no disturbed undercurrents. Clouds lay low down in the west, melted and became twisted by the contrary wind until all that remained were vague shapes very like bloodstained claws groping in the sky. A calm and beautiful evening!

Slowly the eastern sky lost its radiance, and darkened into a blue that already held the grip of a northern summer night. One or two stars appeared, shining pale yet serene in the van of the twilight.

Then Altair heard it — the summons to be away!

Her talons gripped the top of the crag, her neck went forward a little. Swiftly, without a sound, she spread her pinions. As if in harmony with the eager surging of the blood through her veins, the wind leaped on her, lifting her body. Then she was away, up over the plateau, encircling the entire mountain ridge once, twice, and yet again.

Superb and magnificent was she in her effortless gliding that took her higher and higher over her birthplace. Finally, straight as an arrow in its flight, the eagle left forever the crags of Roineval heading direct toward the west and the large white star shining where the sun had been.

Almost as if by experience, she thrust up a full hundred feet as she approached the summit of Beinn Totaig, giving just a slight downward tilt of her pinions as she rode the air currents. Swiftly then, for so young a bird, she sailed away until she was little more than a speck disappearing into the arc of the sky.

She had almost vanished when the old birds came winging in, and Greeka called out in greeting.

Altair saw neither those who were her parents, nor heard the excited cheowping of her brother; she kept to a straight course, reveling in the spin of the wind. Her eyes, oblivious to all but the transparent sky above her, did not register the spread of the earth beneath, the ever-changing panorama of color, of hill and depression, of tiny burns that crisscrossed the moorland, and the gleaming tarns. Then in a burst of excitement, she thrust up higher than ever. All power and ecstasy were hers. She lowered one wing and banked, seeing for the first time the fertile earth slipping away below, with a range of hills in the west overshadowing a loch.

She closed her pinions, and depressing her tail feathers, went into a stoop.

A stalker, after a wild duck on the shore of Loch Duagrich under the windward slope of Braon a' Mheallain, saw the shape of the eagle hurtling down. Less than thirty yards away were some lambs, and the man's immediate reaction was that the bird of prey contemplated an attack.

Then Altair broke the stoop and went thrusting up once again. It was at that precise moment that Falcoo — the cream-breasted peregrine that nested on the irregular ridge of Beinn na Cloiche — took a hand in Altair's affairs. Uttering an angry "Kek, Kek," he came swooping over the ridge. Then like a flash, he winged up after the eagle who, indifferent to his sharp cries, swung a little to one side. Even as the peregrine went rising high above her, Altair keeled over, and closing her pinions once more, came hurtling down in the direction of the loch.

This time, the stalker was confident that she intended snatching one of the lambs. As Falcoo went into a dive after his more formidable adversary, the fellow brought his gun sharply to his shoulder, got the eagle accurately in the sights, and fired.

The crack of the shot echoed across the loch. Falcoo vanished more quickly than he had appeared; wild ducks flew away with piercing calls of alarm; the lambs scattered up the brae bleating with terror; but no outcry came from the eagle. She seemed to break the stoop earthward, opened wide her pinions and began to soar.

"Och! Missed it!" said the stalker savagely.

The crack of the shot still came back to him in receding echoes from the flanks of the hills.

Upward into the solitudes of the skies went Altair, no longer harassed by the falcon, her breast feathers becoming stained with her lifeblood. Up still she went, beyond even the altitude of the wind which had deserted her, driven perhaps by the burning pain in her breast, urged on perhaps by some dim hope of respite in the quiet sky which for so many days had beckoned to her.

The blood-red claws of dissolved cloud that had been low in the west were now directly above the soaring bird, having come in on a contrary current of air. Even as Altair's nature was such that she must search out the mysteries of the uncharted paths of her kind, so now did she fulfil her destiny in this, her last moment of conscious life.

The earth fell away at the stupendous effort she made. Straight through the drift of dissolved cloud she went, the strands now not so red as the feathers on her breast. Then, quite suddenly, it was over.

The upward flight of a dying bird had ended!

Her head which, till then, had been pointed resolutely toward the star whose name she bore, fell on to her breast and a cry came from her. Her body slipped sideways, and instinctively, the immense pinions closed and she went into her last stoop.

That final flight she made had taken her well over the southern slopes of Braon a' Mheallain and the green meadows of Ullinish. Now, instead of the grassland was the sea — calm and unruffled, with the star of the Falconidae held in a pool of still water.

Direct for that pool in the sea came Altair, no longer a proud bird of prey, but a lifeless body seeking its last resting place.

A sea gull, cruising across the bay, saw her approaching and flew off with a querulous note of fear. The cry was still vibrating in the air when the eagle hit the water of the pool, splintering the reflection of the star into a thousand pieces. Ripples broke against the surrounding barrier of the sea — broke, and broke again, until only a slow heaving on the ocean remained. Then, once more, did Altair — the Star of the Falconidae — shine quiet and unmoving in the deep pool where tides did not flow and an eagle had gone to seek peace.

Only the repeated cry of the still frightened gull was Altair's requiem, while high above, the last of the red claws of cloud melted and were gone.

CHAPTER TEN

GREEKA

THE BREAK IN THE WEATHER CAME THE FOLLOWING DAY. A rising wind swept the hitherto calm sea, and the colorful sunset that had given way to a cloudless night saw a perceptible change before dawn which broke angrily with great drifts of cloud gathering in the west. Rain was clearly in the air, and the earth seemed to quicken with anticipation.

Greeka. alone now on the plateau, sat hunched up, watching the cloud shapes coming in from over the coast. Below the sprawl of the mountain ridge, sheep moved restlessly across the moor, and the peewits were in evidence again, calling down the whole length of the glen.

No shadow chased sunshine across the hollows; there was only the hasty nodding of the cotton grass in the wind, and here and there the sharp press of animal feet upon the green bog grass, while over the frowning crags of Roineval the wide sweep of the gray sky emphasized the deep, everpresent loneliness of hills grown gray with the weight of countless centuries.

At last the peewits ceased their calling, and the rain began to fall.

For a while longer, Greeka surveyed the moor, while the rain slanted down full upon him. Then, shaking his plumage, he flew with ease up to the pinnacle that, less than twelve hours before, had been Altair's lookout post.

There had been no conscious preparation on his part. The short flight was a mere expression of his will, prompting him to widen his vision. Moreover, unlike his sister, Greeka was not contemplating a long journey when he started to range the moor. He had much to learn from the old birds before going great distances from Roineval. From them, he wished to learn the secret of successful hunting. After that, his future activities would be dictated by the needs of the moment.

Had he but known it, he was merely keeping to tradition. It had ever been thus with the male eaglet. While it was an all too familiar occurrence for the female to go off afar the moment she could fly, the male habitually remained with the parent birds for quite a period after he had taken to the air. Only with the gradual depletion of the old bird's regular food supplies would they cease to tolerate the eaglet longer and drive him off to fend for himself.

Meanwhile, perfectly comfortable on the pinnacle, Greeka sat awaiting the return of Greesha and Groonah. The rain was falling more heavily now, and the sky was entirely overcast. Already the higher hills were wreathed in trailing skeins of mist, and the burns began to sing out with renewed vitality.

Suddenly Greeka turned his attention to a hollow at the

very foot of the mountain ridge. He stiffened with anticipation.

Scarcely discernible amidst the small boulders, a hare was sitting up with ears twitching nervously and paws held limply across its breast. Its rapid breathing told of the creature's agitation as if it had sensed danger in the wind.

Then Greeka opened his pinions and, from a height of over a thousand feet, launched himself off the pinnacle. For an instant he floated out over the massed rocks on the flank of Roineval, held himself taut in the wind currents, then fell, his wings pressed close to his body.

It was a mere pretence at a stoop, and he alighted some distance from the hare that suddenly doubled up and went zigzagging down the glen.

Greeka made a frantic effort to follow his quarry. His efforts to rise and gain speed at the same time were those of a young bird quite inexperienced in the vagaries of the wind. Everything he did was merely instinctive, possessing none of the cunning that would have characterized the actions of an older bird, grown wise with many years of constant practice.

At last Greeka planed down and came to rest on a boulder close to the burn. Uttering a cry of disappointment, the eagle stood with wings full spread and his head moving from left to right as if with extreme annoyance. Then he relaxed, and sat as serenely on the boulder as he had on the high pinnacle above the plateau.

The rain had drifted off, but the sky was still heavy with further rain to come. Over by Drynoch, it could be seen falling in a veil of gray strands that misted the lower slopes of the hills.

For almost a week, the weather continued unsettled. Often there were whole days when the rain came down in stinging pelts, and heavy clouds from the northwest drove in wind-tossed confusion over the mountains, blotting out the higher peaks and filling the passes with mist. During most of the hours of daylight there was only the cry of sheep on the moor, while toward dusk, which came gray and uncertain, the peewits would start calling once more over Beinn Totaig, and the snipe sounded down by the small loch.

One evening, however, toward the end of the week, the clouds lifted a little, and over the sea, the sky was of a warm primrose color which soon changed to green. By nightfall, the clouds were again racing inland, heavy with rain, and dark night rode upon the summits of the hills where no sound was save the voices of the wind and the innumerable burns.

Greeka was beginning to identify every sound that was brought to him on the wind. Soon he was able to separate one from the other, recognizing the sough of the wind itself in the bog rushes and heather, and learning by its insistent rhythm the varying notes of the burn in spate.

On the very bad nights, he slept soundly enough, with head under wing, and sheltered by the cornerstone of the eyrie which, as the old birds knew from long experience, broke the force of the northwestern winds. Oddly enough, since Altair had gone, Greesha had joined his mate in roosting on the nest, and Greeka accepted the arrangement as a matter of no untoward interest.

Groonah was usually the first to awaken, and, after preening herself, would regard the young bird with a degree of suspicion. She was somewhat perplexed that he did not attempt to join her in flight, but just made for some convenient boulder to await her return with food. Since she no longer used the larder, there was never any reserve of meat as in the past, and she and Greesha had to quarter sufficient territory to support both themselves and the lazy Greeka.

On the morning following the primrose and green sky at sunset, Groonah surveyed the moor still lashed by rain and partially obscured by mist. The wind was high and good for flying.

She gave a gruff bark and roused her mate. She then buffeted Greeka with her pinions until he, too, was thoroughly awake and regarding her with a display of temper at her intrusion into his slumbers.

Groonah then launched herself off the eyrie, soaring around in a wide circle. Her mate followed. Almost at once, Greeka spread his pinions, but instead of soaring, he flapped clumsily, not attempting to ride the air currents, being only concerned in reaching his favorite boulder where he proposed waiting until Groonah returned with his breakfast.

The old birds sensed his intentions, but that morning, as

if by common consent, they did not desire to let him waste
his time in such an idle manner. Groonah made a quick turn
in the wind, swooped below the hapless Greeka startling
him so that he was forced to gain height to avoid colliding
with her.

It was then that the old male bird took a hand in his
son's education. He also banked in the air streams, swooped,
and then rose almost under Greeka's tail. The young bird
began to seek a pitch out of reach of both Groonah and
Greesha. Thus, before he knew it, he was soaring up into
the wind with the old birds planing up a few feet below.

By now, Greeka had got the feel of the air currents, and
realized he need not use his wings. Moreover, he was conscious of a new, yet oddly exciting thrill — becoming one
with the wind, riding with it while it sang in his feathers.

Higher he went, the old birds following him and watching his every move. Because of the mist, he could no longer
see the spread of the moor below; neither could he see the
sprawled ridge of Roineval. Yet he knew exactly where the
mountain was, knew too where the eyrie lay. The instincts
of the old birds were now his own individual instincts. As
he hovered for a brief second, his eyes contracted and the mist
seemed to lose its density. Then, looking with the keenness
of his kind, he saw, sharp in the center of his focused gaze,
but blurring away toward the extreme edges, a runnel of
water on the moor, and beside it, a rabbit!

The next instant something happened. He saw Groonah

swoop downward and knew at the same time that the area of his concentrated gaze was larger than it had appeared at first — saw the rabbit more clearly, a furred creature by the swiftly running stream of water.

Greeka banked to follow Groonah, but before he had completed the turn, she was rising up toward him, the rabbit held in her talons.

This was his first lesson in actual hunting, and he was quick to learn. After the three birds had devoured the rabbit, Groonah and Greesha launched off into an upward stream of air, and Greeka lost no time in following them.

Although he was unfamiliar with much that the old birds did that day, and was not successful in catching game for himself, he did become proficient in planing swiftly down to earth level. In addition, he began to master the air currents, and no longer experienced any sense of fear when sailing high over the moor.

Nevertheless, when evening began to gather in the misty folds of the hills, he was glad to bank toward Roineval; and while the old birds were still busy quartering the ground in the region of Loch Vidigill, Greeka sat on his favorite boulder awaiting their return.

Fine weather came a couple of days later, sunny but chill, with the clouds still coming in from the north and sweeping down over the heights of the Trotternish; and sometimes they passed over the sun, sending shadows racing across the moor.

Despite the sunshine and the glimpse of dry weather, ragged wisps of white cloud often streaked the sky at sundown, usually followed by heavy masses of vapor. It was clear that more rain was falling in the far northwest; sea gulls too were flying inland. Although the peewits were still calling from the glen, for once, the snipe were silent. They squatted in the long bog grass on the shores of Loch Vidigill and remained very still.

Greeka loved the sudden scurrying of the shadows across the moor, loved too the sun that fell so warm and comforting on his back as he sat on his boulder.

More and more did he fly with the old birds, learning their ways, and succeeding at last in making a splendid stoop on a hare as easily as Groonah or Greesha would have done.

Once, when soaring high, he attained a pitch of over two thousand feet, and hung stationary in the pathways of the air. He saw the whole of his world far below — a world of checkered green with here and there a few silver threads which were the burns. He saw also the sweep of Loch Harport and the sea at Bracadale; but more than these, he saw the grim, black frowning peaks of the Cuillins.

Then — on a morning of high wind — he deserted the old birds and flew down the glen, rising over Loch Harport and drifting down the air streams toward Carbost Moor. In a matter of seconds, he crossed the knoblike summit of Preshal

Mor above Talisker, and glimpsed a white house lying amidst the trees.

Greeka flew over the peak, thrilling to the call of the wind and the racing clouds as had other eagles before him.

It was late when Greeka returned at last to the eyrie on Roineval, and he was tired. He had hunted in the wild corries of the Cuillins, and had experienced his first touch of independence.

When he finally slept, close beside Groonah, with Greesha, his father, on the very edge of the nest, it seemed, in his slumber, the grim peaks of the Cuillins were calling him.

To them, soon, he would go, and the eyrie on Roineval would never see him again.

CHAPTER ELEVEN

SUMMER — SUMMER

THE CORN WAS UP IN THE CROFTER'S SKY. IN THE SHEL-
tered hollows — so few indeed on an island known only for
its barrenness — it lay slowly ripening under the warm sunlight. During the long, the very long hours of twilight
which went passing so quietly into the steellike blueness of
a northern night, the moon — coming up aslant over the distant mountains — would make the corn gleam silver-white
like the spearheads which once waved so fiercely over the
misty isle.

On the moor beyond Carbost, the purple of the heather
was deeper than on any other moor in Skye, glowing less
conspicuously, however, where the glen betwixt Beinn
Bhraghad and Sgwr Thuilm intersected the main Cuillin
ridge and the opposite line of hills on which young pines
had been planted by the Forestry Commission.

It was a lovely summer — that summer of Greeka's
adventurous flights into the unknown. That glen, skirting
the Cuillin ridge, was a landmark he grew to know so well,
returning high over it in the dusk of evening as he made his
way back to the eyrie he still occupied on Roineval.

Besides the glen, he learned to know every upward sweep of the land, every outcrop on the hills that led the way back to Bealach Mor. More intriguing, however, than any of these, was the Corrie of the Hart and the burn that flowed past Ruadh Stac beyond which rose the scarred ridge of the mountain, Blaven.

The old birds, although seldom in the nest these days, began to resent Greeka's return to the eyrie each evening. They considered it was time the young bird kept to the territory he quartered in his hours of hunting, and there find himself a suitable nesting site of his own.

It was a fine, bright morning when the old birds finally decided to send Greeka on his way. He had given them sufficient evidence that he was now able to fend for himself, and when he launched off from the nest, both Greesha and Groonah followed close on his tail. As they thrust up at him Greeka was forced to rise to a high altitude, and he sensed that his parents did not wish him to return again to Roineval.

Encountering a favorable stream of air, Greeka was able to keep to a straight course, gliding, for the most part, with the wind. He was soon over Carbost Moor where the old birds ceased harrying him. So intent was he in keeping to the satisfactory air lane he was traveling that Greeka was not aware of the exact moment they left him and headed back to Bealach Mor. Rising up before him were the ragged Cuillin peaks, and the hunting grounds with which he had grown familiar during the past week or so. When the sun took the western trail behind the Trotternish, he would be alone in those grim Cuillin corries, and no more would the quiet evening sky over Bealach Mor see his shape winging to the eyrie on Roineval.

On that same day, at Portnalong, one might note the crofters' corn, golden now that the summer was so far advanced, their calves so soon weaned from their mothers, and the young sheep now shorn of their wool and standing naked beside the ewes who seemed no longer anxious to protect them.

Summer — summer — the golden corn in the haughs, the calves weaned from their mothers, the lambs shorn — and Greeka gone.

That night, only the wind moved across the wastes of Bealach Mor. The stars looked down as, for so many ages, they had looked down on the volcanic crag of Roineval. The burns, the tarns, caught and held their reflections until, at last, they were dimmed by the rising glory of the full moon which shone not only on Roineval, but also upon Clach Glas where, on a ledge, Greeka now slept alone.

The Blaven ridge on which Greeka had taken up residence was, geologically, the most eastern outpost of the Cuillins, and like them, was composed of angular and precipitous peaks of black gabbro rock. It was, moreover, a ridge little frequented by climbers, being isolated on the western slopes by the wild Sligachan glen, and on the east by Loch Slapin. Viewed from all sides, it was, without doubt, a formidable mass of mountain, its corries showing the deep scar of glaciation that had formed them.

Greeka loved the inaccessibility of his new mountain home. During his many journeys to and from the locality, he had grown familiar with the gigantic peaks that surrounded it, and did not seem to miss the wide sweep of moorland that had characterized Bealach Mor and Drynoch.

His first night was spent on the narrow ledge he had visited during his recent flights over the range. It was on the southern shoulder of Clach Glas which, at that point, fell steeply into a rock-strewn corrie that extended to the narrow glen flanking the granite mountain of Ruadh Stac. Rising away beyond Ruadh Stac and Glen Sligachan were the massed peaks of the Cuillin ridge itself, and no more wild and desolate area of rock and bog existed in the whole of Skye.

It was a wonderful night — his first night alone in what was to be his permanent refuge. It was filled with one sound only — the roar of water falling down the steep cliffs of Clach Glas. To Greeka, in his solitude, it was a comforting sound. It was reminiscent of all the things that lay deep-rooted in him, the things that all members of the feathered tribe had accepted as a safeguard to their security.

Slow died the afterglow of the sunset over the distant Western Isles; slow went the light from the sea and the last of the day in the east. Then perceptibly the shadows dropped down lower and lower over the peaks until the glens were dark, and night trod deepest where the walls of mountain lay lost in the lochs and the bogland.

As the moon came up, large and white, the shadows lightened a little, but the night itself was still firmly encamped in the glens, and the moonglow did but serve to emphasize the upward groping of limbs that buttressed the peaks whose heads were in the stars.

Toward midnight, a sharp, strident cry came shuddering up from the distant glen. The call was repeated, and Greeka, stirring on his ledge, raised his head to listen. It was a sound he had never heard before. As he sank once more into sleep, the savage, half-demented cry was again sent echoing through the night; but the eagle did not heed it further. He had accepted it as something habitual to the district.

Soon, however, was he to know the creature that uttered such a far-reaching, challenging screech!

Dawn the next day found Greeka perched on a bastionlike pinnacle on Clach Glas. He was patiently surveying the territory he was beginning to regard as his own special strip of kingdom. Although in his first year, he already possessed strong instincts regarding the rights of those who belonged to his own tribe. He knew that to trespass upon the hunting grounds of others merited punishment, and he therefore sat watching, knowing that on the northern cliffs of Clach Glas a male bird and his mate had their nesting place. It was to witness their line of flight that he sat and waited so patiently. Only by paying attention to the habits of others could he hope to choose as a hunting ground territory which was not already being seriously depleted of game. Equally important to him — a beginner — was the need to act strategically and thus avoid conflict with those who might regard him as an undesirable interloper.

After about half an hour, Greeka's patience was rewarded. He saw both his neighbors set out. They made off down the glen toward Loch Scavaig and Elgol, and the young bird knew then that the locality in the northwest could be claimed as his own.

Nevertheless, Greeka remained on his lofty perch long after the other two birds had made their flight. He was not altogether sure of himself now that he was actually on his own. He sensed that it had been different when, after a day's exciting exploration of the Cuillin corries, he could set his course back along the moorland to Bealach Mor and Roineval.

Memory, based on instinctive reaction when the old birds, his parents, had driven him away, played little or no part at all in his mental ruminations that morning. He had fully accepted the fact that he could no longer regard Roineval as a roosting place. Moreover, he had known for a long while that the day would come when he would be as now — an independent unit in a world that he must know as he had known Bealach Mor if he were to survive.

His sense of uncertainty, therefore, sprang from his keen awareness of isolation more than from lack of confidence in himself and his ability to hunt. Thus he continued to sit on his lofty perch high above the Clach Glas corrie, watching the narrow glen below and the red pile of Ruadh Stac that rose ahead.

A wreath of mist was unfurling over the crooked peak of Garbh-bheinn. Soon it was twisting and breaking away like a thin trail of smoke. Then, at last, the breeze that had scattered it reached the young eagle as he sat on his rocky height. It possessed sufficient power to stir the bird's primaries, and almost at once, Greeka spread his pinions and floated off, flapping a little as he caught a downward current of air sweeping up the glen. A second later, the eagle soared, and passed over the summit of Ruadh Stac, traveling in the direction of Harta Corrie — the Corrie of the Hart.

His previous sense of indecision was gone with flight. He quivered at the touch of the wind on his feathers. Below him, Loch an Athain and the burn that fed it was first on his right, then on his left, as he banked and played in the air currents.

Suddenly he was conscious of flying into an oncoming stream of air. As he beat up against it, he went up between the high walls of Harta Corrie with the serrated peaks of the main ridge approaching nearer with every movement of his well-adjusted pinions. He began to rise, soared up out of the current of air against which he had been battling, and soon was on a level with the crags of Sgurr a' Mhadaidh.

When directly over the summit of the third pinnacle, Greeka suddenly banked, cut a flawless arc in the sky, and then went hurtling downwind — back into the gloom of Harta Corrie.

It was no mere freak of fancy that took Greeka back over the mountain ridge to the corrie. When rising above the singing of the wind, a sound had come to his ear — that same wild, screeching cry that had disturbed his slumbers on the Clach Glas ledge.

As he swooped over the beetling cliffs and leaned a little on the wind, he saw a movement on the floor of the corrie. He gave another short turn, then flew a straight course, his eyes focused on the huge wildcat that was making for a boulder under the eastern cliff of Bidein.

There was something ominous about the creature — a fierce, concentrated viciousness that Greeka had never before encountered.

When he was directly over the loping figure, the eagle closed his pinions and went into a stoop. The young bird was not conscious of wishing to make a kill. The stoop was purely instinctive, the result of the inherent knowledge handed down to him by his ancestors. Like a dark shadow, Greeka dropped down between the vast walls of the surrounding mountains.

Panzeed, as the wildcat was known, heard the swift hurtling of the eagle's body in his direction. In a flash, he reared up on his hind legs, his jaws wrinkled in a snarl of defiance, his green eyes glaring with anger.

Greeka, acting with extraordinary suddenness, broke the stoop and passed downwind, causing the cat hastily to turn about. Then again, with surprising ease, Greeka had mounted into the wind, turned, and came back to renew his assault on the animal that now he knew to be an enemy. Even as he made the quick turn, he dropped to a lower altitude with legs and talons extended.

The cat spat at him and stabbed upward with his knife-like claws. Once more Greeka swung away, banked, and returned.

Panzeed, moved by extreme cunning, sank back on his haunches and prepared to leap upward. Every muscle in his sinuous body was tensed for the effort he meant to make. Greeka, however, despite his inexperience, depressed his tail feathers and slipped into the wind; and the leap Panzeed had hoped to make was checked by the hiss of the bird's wings within an inch of his head.

This frightened the cat. He had glimpsed the eagle's talons, and sensed that, at close quarters, the advantages would be with the bird. Lord of the Corrie as he supposed himself to be, Panzeed had no desire to come to an inglorious end within sight of his lair. As Greeka turned to drive down upon him once more, the cat, swifter than the bird of prey, sprang under the overhang of a boulder where he lay with wrinkled lips and twitching claws.

Greeka immediately encircled the spot, gave a gruff bark, then was away — flying off down the corrie toward the small loch and the Sligachan burn. Within a matter of seconds he had forgotten the wildcat and was industriously quartering the rough, boulder-strewn ground between Ruadh Stac and the mountain, Marsco.

It was not long before he made a stoop on a buck rabbit, and rising rapidly, made off for his ledge on Clach Glas.

When later that same morning Greeka took a short flight up the Corrie of the Hart, the hollow lay in heavy shadow. A mass of black cloud had passed over the sun, and gloom added to the desolation of rock and bog set in the amphi-theatre of the mountains.

CHAPTER TWELVE

THE ANTAGONISTS

PANZEED, THE WILDCAT, HAD DWELLED IN THE CORRIE of the Hart for many years. In fact, he had known no other home. Completely ruthless with any creature who attempted to outwit him, and by far the cleverest hunter in the glen, he had grown large and sleek, and reigned supreme in that wild district of mountain and burn. Never, till that morning when Greeka had driven him to seek refuge under a boulder, had he known cause for fear. Now, due to his alarming encounter with the eagle, he sensed that his security was threatened and his own particular domain invaded by one who would be difficult to overthrow. Because of the sudden fear he had experienced, for the first time in his life Panzeed began to show definite signs of caution. Instinctively, on leaving his lair after his encounter with Greeka, he crouched low to the ground, his eyes staring upward, for he guessed that it was from above that his enemy would assuredly come.

Like all creatures of the feline tribe, Panzeed was an animal who never forgot, nor forgave an injury. Thus, within a matter of hours of his arrival in Glen Sligachan, Greeka, the eagle from Roineval, had made for himself an enemy that was as dangerous as he was cunning.

The wildcat was, fortunately, the only one of his species in the district.

His mother, a little before he was born, had appeared suddenly from across the narrows of Kyle Rhea.

She had been a braw, vicious creature; about twice the size of a domestic cat, her very appearance was a good indication of her lawless nature. With very short ears, set close on her skull, and a snarl almost permanently wrinkling her lean muzzle, she had, previous to leaving the mainland, terrorized the entire animal kingdom of Coire Domhain.

It had been a somber enough place — that place she knew as home and where she dwelled with a mate whose fierceness nigh outmatched her own. The gloomy coire was formed by a ridge some three thousand feet high thrusting out eastward from the summit of Sgurr Fhuaran, and the lair of the wildcats was placed deep in a rugged retaining wall that boldly supported the mountain.

Pareen, as the mother of Panzeed was known, together with her mate Pazeet, ceaselessly waged war on every living creature living in the glen, even to the extent of attacking deer that, at times, came down off the mountains of Glen Shiel.

Many were the tales that the shepherds and stalkers told when gathered in the old Shiel House Inn at the foot of the glen.

One of the tales, related more often than any of the others, concerned the joint attack Pareen and Pazeet were reputed to have made upon an ancient stag they apparently surprised and drove from a drinking pool.

Local tradition had it that the stag came down off Sgurr na Ciste Duibhe — the Peak of the Black Chest — into the pass of the White Torrent. The day had gone fast a-dying over the western sea when the stag reached the pass and stood, at last, before a small lochan black as the eye of night. He could not have come to the pool at any other time, for keepers had been up the glen, and no sign of any deer had they seen as they set off for Invershiel, and the evening then almost come, with a bright new moon rising high over the massed peaks of the Five Sisters of Kintail.

For a long time the stag must have stood before the tarn, for next morning, a stalker, early abroad on the mountains, came down off the saddle ridge to the drinking pool and saw the creature's footprints set extraordinarily deep in the gravel — a thing that could not have happened had the animal stood for a few moments to drink. The stalker said that he had been puzzled until he noticed, quite close to the water's edge, some further imprints — clearly those of a wildcat. They also were set deep in the gravel as if, like the deer, the cat, too, had stood for a very long time without moving.

There seemed only one possible solution to the problem. The cat had challenged the stag!

What had happened to defeat the cat's purpose was quite beyond the stalker's power to imagine. Of course, a couple of eagles, late making for their eyrie up on Sgurr Fhuaran, might have disturbed the cat, but even that possibility was hardly likely if it was quite dark when the stag and the cat stood motionless in enmity. No eagle, as well the stalker knew, would be abroad in the darkness. Yet, it was clear that something untoward had happened. A trail of footprints, broken and badly blurred, led away from the pool, showing only too clearly that the cat had made a hasty retreat.

The stag had made his departure from the pool no less speedily, his footprints, however, because of his heavier build and size, being more distinctly seen than those of his would-be attacker, and going in the opposite direction.

As the stalker followed the stag's spoor up the glen, he little realized that another discovery was about to be made. He had all too easily assumed that the stag had escaped and had gone back up the hill where he would be safe with the herd. Then the man stopped, his heart, as he said to his friends some hours later, almost in his mouth. For — under the frowning crags of the Peak of the Spaniards — he came upon the stag, still on his feet, but stark dead. The animal was as rigid as a rock, and it was obvious that he had been dead many hours. Because the hapless creature showed no visible sign of injury, the stalker was forced to the conclusion that the magnificent beast had died from sheer fright.

After that, the fellow wasted no further time in the glen, but returned as quickly as he could to Invershiel to obtain assistance and bring the stag's body down to the shooting lodge at the head of the loch.

A couple of hours, maybe three, was the time it took, but when he and two others came back to the Peak of the Spaniards, the body of the deer had been badly mutilated, and it required no expert knowledge to determine that it had been done by two enormous wildcats, for their footmarks were everywhere evident.

The mystery of the stag's death remained unsolved, but it was generally understood that all through the night he had been held at bay by the two cats who, possessed with endless patience, had probably crouched less than a few feet away, and remained completely unmoving until the terrorized beast had died from exhaustion and fear. Moreover, it was highly possible that the wildcats had not been far off when the stalker made his discovery, and immediately he had departed, they set about their gruesome feasting, leaving little but hide and bones as evidence of their presence.

It seemed quite possible that the innkeeper at Invershiel was right when he said that the cat's hasty retreat from the pool had been little more than an effort to startle the stag. Then perhaps, with the assistance of his mate, an attempt had been made to drive the creature up the glen to a spot considered more suitable for the kill. That they had indeed succeeded was vouched for by more than just the stalker who had first made the discovery, and not once did the story lose anything in the telling.

It was, however, during the spring of the following year that Pareen lost her mate, and herself avenged his death in a manner that rid the glen of the badger family for many seasons to come.

That spring of Pazeet's untimely passing from the scene of his many vicious triumphs was the beginning of the great blizzard that was to last for over a month. Just when it seemed that the warmer weather was on the way, a keen northerly air stream came down from off the mountains of Sutherland, and soon, all the country, north of the Great Glen, was under a thick covering of ice and snow.

The gloomy corrie where the wildcats dwelt was completely cut off, and a high ridge of ice separated it from the less-exposed regions adjacent to Loch Duich. The River Croe was also under a covering of ice, and no longer could fish be found in the many rock pools. As a result, famine came to all those creatures whose lairs were on the northern buttress of that retaining wall of the mountain, Sgurr Fhuaran.

It was a dark, bitter night when Pazeet set out on what was to be his last hunting expedition. The snow was hard beneath his feet, and the wind was driving down the glen like a many-tailed whip. Both he and his mate were starving, and there was murder in his heart when he made for the old glen road and the small copse where he knew a badger sett to be.

More than once Pazeet stopped close to where a boulder or some outcrop of rock afforded him shelter from the wind. More than once he hesitated as if to return to his lair in Coire Domhain. The pangs of hunger, however, would persist in reminding him that there was nothing left to hunt in that gloomy corrie on the northern slope of the mountain; thus he continued on his way, following the downward run of the wind as it swept along the wide strath of Glen Shiel.

Once he thought he heard a stag belling way up on the summit of Sgurr na Carnach, but when he paused to listen, nothing at all could be heard but the whistling of the wind and, afar off, the roar of it as it struck the little copse where the badgers lived.

Pazeet moved on, using his nose and traveling slowly so as to avoid giving warning of his approach.

Through a break in the cloud masses above the Five Sisters, a star flickered fitfully, and Cheekee, the ancient owl who lived in a tree above the badger's home, saw it and gave out a sound that was scarcely the hoot he usually uttered. Like all others in the glen, he too was starving, and on seeing the glimmer of the star all he could do was give out that throaty cry almost as if he were calling out to the star. Way over on the edge of the copse, another of his kind heard him and also cried out. The star flickered a few moments longer then was gone — lost once more behind the never ending drift of cloud brought down from the north by the Arctic wind.

Suddenly Cheekee straightened and prepared to launch himself into the wind. Then he settled back on his perch again, recognizing in the darkness the shape of old Brock who was setting out in the hope of finding food for the young he had hidden away in the sett.

The badger was experiencing the same difficulty as Pazeet. In all the wide waste of the glen there was nothing left for him to hunt.

Brock had scarcely been a few minutes on his way when the wildcat suddenly sprang on him from behind. He let out a muffled cry of fear, causing Cheekee to leave his perch and fly off into the very smore of the blizzard.

From the very first moment of the attack, both animals fought with a tenacity born of hunger and fear, and the glen echoed with Pazeet's shrill screams and Brock's hoarse grunts.

The battle must have gone on for most of the night, for scarcely an hour went by but that a terrifying scream rent the air, or a savage grunt was caught up by the wind and tossed, like an agonized cough, far into the darkness.

That night the wind blew itself out, and the last of the snow went scudding over the peaks and glens of Sutherland and Ross-shire. Morning, however, was gray and wan as had been the mornings for many a week past; but behind the grayness, blue skies were surely breaking through as the thinning clouds lifted a little from the mountains. There was even a slow-moving finger of light traveling up the rock face of Beinn Fhada as the day grew stronger, making the crystalized snow on the summit glisten.

It was a couple of hours after daybreak when Pareen, picking up her mate's trail, came over the mountain pass below the shoulder of Sgurr na Carnach, and headed straight down the glen in the direction of the copse. That was the hour when the light moving up the face of Beinn Fhada was at its brightest and the snow began to gleam out.

A hungry buzzard flew mewling high above Pareen, followed by an eagle who wheeled slowly over the Peak of the Black Chest. Pareen snarled as she loped, with nose to the ground, toward the scene of the night's conflict. Yet, keen though her senses were, no indication did she have of her mate's fate, despite the buzzard who continually called high above her, and the eagle who never ceased wheeling over the Peak of the Black Chest.

Then, as the finger of light on Beinn Fhada suddenly departed, leaving the mountain dark and brooding, she came upon her mate and Brock, both dead, each with their claws sunk deeply into the other.

All around, the displaced snow, red with the blood that had been shed, told Pareen of the bitter struggle that had been waged unceasingly until death had intervened. The bereaved cat stood for some minutes as if unable to realize that her mate of many seasons was no more. Then, giving a shrill scream, she proceeded to rend what remained of Brock until he was an unrecognizable mass of fur. Her mate she tried to drag away, but finding the task beyond her strength, she dug into the snow, and by making good use of her hind legs, almost succeeded in covering the body.

Then, moved to bitter hatred of the Brock family, and not content with what she had already done to Pazeet's slayer, she made with all haste to the badger sett, and finding the recently born young without protection, dug them out of their refuge and slew them one after another.

When she returned to her lair on the northern slopes of the mountains, she went by a different route, and never paused until the copse and the fatal glen were far behind.

Although she knew it not, Pareen's own sojourn in the neighborhood of Coire Domhain under the shadow of the Five Sisters of Kintail was swiftly drawing to a close. Because she was aware that in the near future she would have young to support, she took greater risks in her hunting, and one evening climbed aboard a small fishing craft moored at the pierhead below Invershiel.

It was a motor-driven vessel from Kyle Rhea on the Isle of Skye, and the well in the stern was laden with baskets of freshly caught fish.

Pareen ate voraciously, and finding a dark corner under a pile of dry net and rope, curled up and slept. The even pulsing of the motor wakened her at last, by which time the craft was well down the loch. Sensing the presence of man whom she feared, she burrowed a little deeper under the net and rope, then lay very quiet and still, waiting for the vessel to stop before attempting to make her escape.

Straight down Loch Duich went the vessel, and passing the small island at the mouth of Loch Long, thrust southward into Loch Alsh, moving in the direction of the narrows of Kyle Rhea. In the swift ebbing and flowing of the tides, the craft swayed perilously, and Pareen, driven by an even greater sense of fear, dug still further under her covering of net and rope.

She had no knowledge of time, being only aware of the swaying of the boat that kept her continually in fear.

At last, after what seemed hours, the craft began to move close inshore, passing a small lighthouse and edging slowly toward Kyle Rhea.

It was quite dark when, guided by lamplight, the small craft moved up to the pier and finally stopped. Even before the boatman could make the vessel fast alongside, Pareen had emerged from her hiding place.

She crouched ready to spring, and the very instant she saw firm ground within leaping distance, she was up and away, and did not stop running until she stood in a boulder-strewn gully that struck from east to west along the slopes of Beinn Bhuidhe. In such a manner came Pareen — the wildcat of Coire Domhain — to the Isle of Skye.

It was raining heavily that night she made her escape to the long gully by Glen Arroch, and the bad weather continued for many days until the entire ravine was little better than a burn in full spate.

Pareen's stay on the slopes of Beinn Bhuidhe, however, was not of long duration. The mountain was too close to the small township of Kyle Rhea, and there were always shepherds moving up into the hills. Thus she began to move farther and farther into territory that grew wilder and more remote with every mile she traveled. Rabbits were scarce on these rock-bound wastes, and she grew thin. Hunting as best she could, and often feasting on carrion left by the crows, she finally crossed the old drove road west of Lochan Dubha and approached the wide strath of Suardal, beyond which rose the Red Hills and the deer forest of Lord MacDonald.

She was reaching country she recognized as similar to that which she had known but a short while before, and on the very morning when she came down off the hill of Glas Bheinn Mhor and entered the wild and desolate glen of Sligachan, she was aware that her long trek over the hills was at an end. That same day, she found a satisfactory lair in the gloomy Corrie of the Hart, and lined it with old bracken in readiness for the young she soon would have.

There, to the distant sound of water falling from off the black shoulders of Bidein, Panzeed was born, the only one of her kittens to survive the hardships she had undergone since Pazeet's death. There, long after Pareen herself had departed into the hunting grounds of the lost to seek out her mate, Panzeed had lived and thrived, with none to dispute his sovereignty of the glen until Greeka, the eagle from Roineval, came to dwell on Clach Glas.

From that very day, they were enemies!

CHAPTER THIRTEEN

MONARCH OF THE HIGH HILLS

PANZEED'S TERRITORY EXTENDED RIGHT UP THE GLEN, AND he hunted both sides of the Sligachen River which was bounded in the west by the precipitous crags of Sgurr nan Gillean, and in the east by the scree slopes of Beinn Dearg — the ranging ground of herds of red deer.

The wildcat, however, never traveled beyond the near slopes of the mountain deer forest, and therefore never saw any of its inhabitants. He was nevertheless fully aware that Beinn Dearg was the haunt of deer, and this knowledge was his by reason of the belling that came floating off the mountain when Rooloo, Lord of the Herd, sounded his defiance on those evenings when the world was at peace, and stalkers were absent from the hill.

Greeka often heard the stag belling when he sat on his ledge above the Clach Glas corrie. Having no previous experience of wild deer, since no herds had been in the neighborhood of Bealach Mor, he was curious about the beast who sounded such a challenging note. Thus, early one morning as the sun came up over the mountains of the mainland,

Greeka left his nesting place and made for the barren slopes
of Lord MacDonald's Forest.

Panzeed, that morning, was nowhere visible, and as a result Greeka was not tempted away from the course he was
pursuing. He passed leisurely over the summit of Marsco,
and the glen below was an intricate pattern of burns, lochans
and boulders.

A favorable stream of air enabled him to glide along the
whole mountain range until finally he was soaring high over
the cone-shaped summit of Glamaig — the most northerly
spur of the forest. Then suddenly he banked, and, coming
straight back over the scree slopes of Beinn Dearg, saw Rooloo
standing guard over his herd on the plateaulike ridge of the
escarpment.

Although Greeka was now flying directly into the wind,
the speed of his flight from one point to another had not
lessened, and only once did he use his pinions, giving a de-
liberate downward stroke as if to propel him just a little more
quickly to the spot where the stag was standing.

Greeka was reveling in the steadiness of the flight he was
making. The whaleback ridge of the mountain shaped the
wind currents, and they came at him strong and chill, passing over and under him with an intimacy he enjoyed. Then,
in an excess of delight, he thrust up, wings gathered about
him, spun around, and came gliding back toward the watching stag.

Since there were no calves among the herd, Rooloo was

not unduly disturbed by the presence of the eagle. He merely observed the bird's aerobatics from a vantage point that, amongst other things, enabled him to watch for any suspicious movement on the floor of the glen below.

Greeka finally alighted on a spur of rock some hundred yards away, and stood quietly watching the hinds. Since they were a little restless at the presence of the huge bird on their mountain sanctuary, Rooloo moved forward a few paces, ready to give battle to the eagle should he essay an attack.

When he found that the herd was not menaced, the stag took up a position a little to the windward of the hinds and was thus in direct line with Greeka. He was a ten-pointer, with a fine wide head. As he stood motionless with his head held high, he presented a magnificent sight, with the fall of the mountain behind him, and the pinnacled peaks of the Black Cuillins rising up way across the glen.

Like Panzeed, the wildcat, Rooloo had dwelt in the neighborhood for over eleven stalking seasons. During his seventh year, he had met with an injury from a stalker's stray shot.

A little of that memory might have been moving in him that morning when Greeka came sailing high overhead, for on that fateful day there had been an eagle swooping in low from the direction of Loch Ainort, and rising suddenly when the shot that was fired went echoing over the mountains.

From force of habit, the stag flared the air currents now. No disturbing taint was in it, and save for the eagle, he and the herd were alone.

Meanwhile, Greeka had begun to preen his feathers. He was happy on that spur of rock high up on Beinn Dearg. The wind had a bite in it he liked, and he sensed that there might be good hunting way beyond the eastern slopes in the green strath of A Coire nan Brucdarun.

Rooloo watched the eagle without enmity.

In the memory of experiences in Rooloo's past was the shape of the eagle coming in low up Coire nan Brucdarun, and the bird's sudden swoop into the air at the sound of the shot. All were closely associated with one thing — the shattering of his hind leg! Irrevocably bound up with this impression was the call the eagle gave when Rooloo himself flung up his head at the pain he experienced.

To the stag, in the overwhelming fear that had assailed him, it seemed that the bird was endeavoring to warn him of further danger, and that the only sure way of escape lay in one direction — that which the eagle had taken.

There was a run of clean wind over the mountain that day, and those that sought the stag's destruction were not betrayed by it. Thus Rooloo accepted the only course open to him. He struggled as best he could down an acclivity that led to the isolated pass between the forked burn and the lower slopes of Belig.

The slow movement of animal reactions connecting the present with the past and the past with the present were no more than mild ripples such as might be seen on the wind-ruffled surface of a mountain tarn. Yet each ripple, containing as it did some vibration of the past, brought clearly into focus the particular event in the stag's life that was intimately connected with it.

Thus as he stood that morning on Beinn Dearg watching Greeka preening himself, with the steep fall of the mountain behind him, and no alien movement on the floor of the glen to disturb the calm he felt, Rooloo relived, in a protective reaction, the most outstanding event in his past — the one brought so vividly alive in his mind by the sudden appearance of the eagle.

The picture, wrought on the canvas of the present with so uncompromising a realism, sent a quiver along the stag's spine. He felt once again the hurt in his leg, and it was almost as though he were moving with great distress down the scree slope he had traversed on that fateful day of the wounding. Under the stress of that moment, so startlingly conveyed on the mirror of his animal consciousness, his nose began instinctively to search the air currents as if seeking in them a clue to the position of those who desired his destruction; and even as on that very day when his leg had been shattered by the bullet, the wind that had brought Greeka over the mountain was just as clean, with no stain in it to tell him what he wished to know.

Greeka, on his distant boulder, had ceased preening his feathers, and stood poised for flight.

Rooloo seemed no longer aware of him. Even during the slow spreading of the eagle's wings, the stag was moving through an experience of time far removed from the present, an experience that had taken place under a sunless sky and on another stretch of hillside.

Down toward the forked burn he seemed to be going, dragging the injured leg, yet moving quickly because of the rising fear in him, and because he had been unable to find in the clean race of the wind the knowledge that might have aided him in his escape.

There was no track down the hillside. Once he stopped, and saw, way over the shoulder of the hill, two hinds standing headlong to the wind. As Rooloo looked over at them, he was aware that the wind had lost its keenness and was suddenly little more than a thin, quiet trickle of air wandering across the scree slopes like a lost thing. Then a stone rattling down toward him caused Rooloo to take immediate fright. He tossed his head and snorted, and stumbled on some distance before he stopped again, this time not to look for the hinds, who had disappeared, but to stare back the way he had come, to satisfy himself that he had shaken off whoever had loosened the stone in his direction.

Nobody could he see, and no suspicious movement was there on the serrated ridge high above, which ran sharply upward to a conical peak.

His heart beat in heavy thuds; his nostrils flared widely to take in the cool air of the mountain. There, in the remote silence, Rooloo felt cut off from his kind, from his world.

He was nervous, for in the silence was danger. Man was hidden somewhere, perhaps behind the ridge. His shattered, aching leg was evidence of that.

Once again his nostrils flared widely to take in the air; then, treading delicately, and grunting as movement caused the wound to sting and bleed anew, he continued on downhill, placing each forefoot carefully so that no sudden falling away of the scree should bring him to his knees. Uppermost now in him was the desire to reach a place of sanctuary under Glas Bheinn Mhor where he had been born.

The slope became steeper. The last mile or so off the mountain were going to be the hardest he had yet encountered. Already, despite the care he took, the scree began to fall away at every step he made, and the pain in his hind leg was becoming increasingly worse.

The sunless sky grew darker; there was low cloud now breaking over the serrated ridge high above. Rooloo seemed to be in a two-dimensional world — a world of mist and sky above, and a boulder-strewn world below. There was, however, another world beyond the boulders which he could not see — the pleasant green world of the strath, where grew coarse grass sweet to the tongue, and banks of purple heather soft to the flank. Because of that other world, he pressed on, and finally came off the mountain and stood amidst the boulders.

Yet another half hour was to pass by before he reached

the desolation of the forked burn where, in the quietness, he lay down for a while and attempted to lick the wound which was now bleeding freely.

The dampness of the ground beneath the press of his body was a comforting respite, bringing a chill relief to the throbbing muscles so sorely tried during his perilous descent off the mountain.

Then, just when he felt completely relaxed, a blackcock rose a few feet away and startled him so badly that he was once again on the move, this time making, with an uncanny knowledge of its exact position, for the sanctuary that lay far across the strath and under the shadow of a hill.

Although the stag had not been aware of the fact, it must have rained during the night, for the northern fork of the burn was in spate, and the roar of the torrent over the stones and the boulders was a comforting reminder that he was now far away from those who had been stalking him, and that his coveted sanctuary was not a great distance off.

He drank deeply from the burn, lifting his head high as if to aid his swallowing. Drops of blood falling from the wound momentarily caused a crimson stain to flow away on the run of the water. Rooloo, once again aware of the tearing ache in his leg, swung his long neck around, and, with a tongue moist with his drinking, patiently licked and licked until the ache was soothed and the blood ceased to flow.

The wind now was blowing up the strath toward him. It was still clean, the only scent in it being that of bog grass.

Rooloo continued on his journey across the strath, coming at last to a place of rocks set between the slopes of Belig and the hooked peak of Garbh-bheinn on the Blaven-Clach Glas range. It seemed an eternity before he found himself facing a deep rock pool with the high banks of a burn giving way to a tract of sodden ground. Beyond was the tough grass that, in his younger days, had been so sweet to the tongue.

He stood in a moment of breathless tension lest this should not be the place after all.

Then all his anxiety fell away from him; in that same moment, there departed from him all the terror of the chase. He had made no mistake in his traveling. This was his refuge, for there, in a loop of the burn, was the grassy green hollow where he had been born — the hollow known from time immemorial as Tir nan Og, the Land of Youth!

From the very first day when the red deer of the Highlands found themselves in need of a sanctuary from man, this was the place they chose, and there they brought forth their young and lived in peace. To this very spot in his seventh year came Rooloo — Lord of the Forest of Beinn Dearg — to rest while Nature, the great healer, mended the broken bone in his leg and took away the ache from the torn flesh.

All so clear now that memory of the past, a memory of peace and contentment in a place that was full of silence save for those sounds habitual to it — the soft cry of the wind and the silver-voiced song of the burn.

The stag, his body close-pressed against the earth that had

nourished him from birth, felt the flow of its secret life force, and as he lowered his head to rest, Nature began her great work of healing.

Rooloo had almost closed his eyes when he was conscious of something dark and with widespread pinions sweeping up over him. In a moment the past had vanished into the immediate necessity of the future.

Greeka, the eagle from the Clach Glas ridge, had taken to wing and was soaring upward into the open pathways of the air.

Rooloo's excursion into the past had been but a brief incident in the passing of time, for during it, the eagle had no more than spread his pinions and launched himself from the boulder.

In a matter of seconds, during which Rooloo turned his attention to the herd, Greeka, having decided to visit the wildcat's territory before hunting in the green strath of A Coire nan Brucdarun, had taken up his position on a crag, and waited patiently for some sign of Panzeed.

The cat himself was well aware of Greeka's constant vigilance in Harta Corrie. He knew that between them existed bitter enmity and in their struggle the age-old law of the wild would prevail — the survival of the fittest!

Panzeed was hungry that day as he lay in his lair dug deep under a boulder. His night hunting had not been profitable, and he knew from various castings he had found that the eagle had been active a few hours previous, with the result that rabbits, his main diet, seemed unusually wary.

For a long time the cat lay with his body curled into a ball of fur, his nose sunk into his tail. Occasionally he opened his eyes and twitched his ears at some sound outside.

A long way off, he could hear the bleating of sheep; somewhere, up the corrie, a sea gull mewed like a kitten. As he stared up at the narrow opening of the lair, he saw a cloud of midges fluttering in the sunlight, and the constant movement annoyed him. Finally, he yawned, and once again relaxed, and slept.

Suddenly he was wide awake and savagely alert!

A slight sound — quite different from those other sounds he associated with the lair — had come to him, bringing into play the instinctive reaction preparatory to his attempting a kill. The sound was repeated — nearer this time so it seemed — and Panzeed, forgetting the eagle, crept forward, his body almost touching the ground and his nose testing the air.

There — less than five yards from his refuge — was a sea gull. The bird was standing on a small rock, within easy leaping distance of Panzeed's sinuous figure.

The cat crouched back on his hind legs, ready to spring. His teeth were displayed in a vicious snarl, and his ears closely pressed against his lean, malevolent skull. Only one desire dominated his feline consciousness — the desire to slay the unsuspecting sea bird.

Then just as his paws were leaving the ground, a dark

shadow swept across the sky. The sea gull spread its wings and was away with a querulous cry of fear.

At the suddenness of the occurrence, Panzeed turned turtle in the midst of the leap that was taking him upward. The shadow above him raced past and as quickly returned. No ordinary shadow this, that caused the wildcat such panic. Panzeed, diving into the mouth of the den, saw out of the corner of one eye the shadow sweeping down upon him.

Greeka — the silent — whose very swiftness in the air was his shield against the cunning of the cat, seemed like a bronze thunderbolt as he hurtled toward his enemy.

Even as Panzeed in fear and consternation quickly turned about in his lair, the shadow departed. When, a split second later, the cat looked out of the entrance to the den, all he saw was a quivering glow of light that gathered and became still as Greeka, on outstretched wing, made off down the corrie toward the glen and the green strath beyond Beinn Dearg.

Panzeed was able to interpret the reason for the steady glow of light in which the midges were again congregating. There was no movement outside to disturb it; no oblique line of gloom cast by the figure of one who sat on an outcrop and waited.

Confidence in himself was again restored, and being urged by the desire to assuage the hunger he felt, the cat emerged cautiously from the lair.

All he saw was Greeka rising steadily in the air at the head of the corrie, then banking gracefully as he slipped into a favorable flow of wind.

Rage at the eagle's repeated intrusion into his territory held the cat completely impotent for a second or two. Then, digging his claws savagely into the ground, he gave vent to a piercing scream, his tail waving furiously, and his eyes glaring with defiance.

Greeka, however, was too immersed in other pleasures just then to heed the wildcat further. Coming off the heights of Beinn Dearg sounded the belling note of Rooloo — Monarch of the High Hills.

The stag continued to call long after Panzeed had become silent and was stalking with care a rabbit that dared to frolic in the grim Corrie of the Hart.

CHAPTER FOURTEEN

WHEN THE HUNTING WINDS ARE LOOSE

SUMMER ENDED SUDDENLY THAT YEAR. ON THE VERY DAY when it seemed that the warm, sunny weather was likely to continue indefinitely, the skies became overcast. Vast banks of cloud rose up in the west, and high, tempestuous seas drove in on the Atlantic coasts. That same night, heavy rains came to Skye and lasted for almost a week. When they eventually ceased, mists hung low over the entire island, and the mountains, both north and south, were hidden in a gray blanket that muffled all sound and reduced visibility on the moors to a few yards.

Yes, indeed! Summer had truly gone, and the long Hebridean winter was at hand.

For the moment, however, although winter was marshaling its forces in the north, it had not yet sent to Skye its advance brigades of bitter wind and sleet. Thus, during the month of October — the month of the hunting winds — deer stalkers were out on the hills.

Greeka often quartered the high hills and adjacent moors these days. It was while exploring the moorland between

Glamaig and Loch Sligachan that he saw men traveling along the old track that went from north to south along the eastern slopes of Lord MacDonald's Forest. With them were ponies.

The eagle was perturbed. Movement up into the hills always alarmed him, and he instinctively distrusted man.

His distrust grew when, late in the afternoon, he saw the stalkers returning, bringing in their victim — a fine, well-pointed stag, slung lifeless over the back of one of the ponies.

Greeka rose hurriedly from the boulder where he had been feasting on a rabbit. The stag reminded him of Rooloo. With the remembrance came other impressions. He noticed how the mist stood unmoving in the hollows between the hills, how the stalkers and the pony bearing the stag seemed scarcely real as they moved steadily along the flanks of the mountain, with the trail running on ahead like a thin, twisty thing that had neither beginning nor ending.

The eagle banked and swung out a little over the valley until the mountains of the deer forest were behind him, and Loch Ainort directly below. He banked again, and returned, hearing, as he came in low, a heron crying out across the wind-whitened waters of Loch Sligachan, hearing too the roar of a torrent down the slopes of Glamaig upon which the stag had been slain.

Twice, in the space of a few seconds, that heron cried out across the loch. When it seemed the evening had grown quiet after its calls, and Greeka encircled once more the area of the track along which the small party was still moving, a Highland bull bellowed in lamenting tones.

The stalker, leading the pony bearing the stag, found himself thinking how queer it all was — almost like the living mourning the passing of something that had belonged to their world of dawn and dusk, of noonday heat and sun, of rain and wind-swept mountain.

The mountain itself was now darkening with the fast oncoming night. A heavy cloud dropped slowly over the summit. Only Greeka, encircling the strath, witnessed the departure of the stag from the haunts he had known.

No lamenting bellows from the bull now; no heron crying across the wind-whitened waters of the loch. Yet, from afar off there did sound a last trumpeting call for the stag — a call winding down from the mist-draped heights of Beinn Dearg from one of his own kind. Then silence, the stalkers and the pony with its burden gone, no eagle in the darkening sky, just the silence and the hunting winds temporarily stilled.

Greeka was abroad early next morning. As he swung off Clach Glas and spiraled over the peak of Garbh-bheinn, he reveled once again to the touch of the wind in his feathers. Then straight across Strath na Creitheach he went, catching the wild spin of the wind over the summit of the mountain, Marsco, then riding a downwind channel of air that carried him over a narrow glen of many burns to the scree slopes of Beinn Dearg Mheadhonach. No hinds were visible on the mountain that morning, but as he made his way leisurely across the broad whalelike ridge, Greeka did see Rooloo, standing almost hidden in the cleft of Bealach na Spairde where, the previous day, one of his race had fallen a victim to a stalker's well-directed shot.

That morning, since the spin of the wind was in his favor, Greeka made no attempt to alight on Beinn Dearg, but flew straight on until he was directly over the schoolhouse at Sconser and held in the stiff flow of the air currents from off Loch Sligachan. As he leaned on the wind, he saw men and ponies turning off the lochside road, and heading up the old stalkers' track.

Sea gulls, however, were wheeling and swooping over the loch, attracted by a run of trout, and their excited calls drew the eagle's attention away from the men bent on another hunting expedition. From his higher pitch above the sea gulls, Greeka could see the movement of the fish below the water.

He went into a stoop, but finding the sea-birds' sport not to his liking, he flattened out, and moving on the wind currents, passed over the loch and did not break his flight until he hung poised over the Isle of Raasay where he finally spent the day hunting rabbits on the hill of Dun Caan.

It was early in the evening when he returned, flying high across Kyle More and approaching Glamaig from a point almost due east. The wind was now against him, and he used his wings to keep himself evenly balanced.

Although clouds were drifting in from the main Cuillin

ridge, mist had not quite obscured the sprawling massif of the deer forest.

The strong veering of the wind over the summit of Glamaig set Greeka on a straight course along the undulating back of Beinn Dearg. While the light on the mountain was no longer good, his keen eyes picked out the stealthy movement of stalkers still actively engaged in making their way toward the southern retaining cliffs directly opposite Marsco.

Maybe it was another cross current of wind caught up between the two mountains that suddenly lifted the eagle so that he went sailing up the narrow glen that separated the deer forest from its near neighbor over which low cloud was tumbling away into mist.

As he went drifting easily on the flaw of the wind, with the glen below rising half a thousand feet in as many yards, he heard curlews piping. Then, far off, he saw them, wheeling wide and tireless over what seemed a small tarn, gray and remote amidst a wilderness of rock and boulder.

Suddenly the eagle found that he was flying out of the wind, planing down between the walls of scree and rock. The afternoon light, long since faded to little more than a dim twilight in the glen, was chill and uninviting.

Indeed, Greeka was suddenly aware of wanting to reach his nesting site on Clach Glas, and would have flown out of the glen but for the dark shadow moving down the slopes of Beinn Dearg. At the same instant that the eagle marked the slow downward movement of the shadow, he swung off toward the cliffs of Marsco where he suddenly came to rest with a soft fluttering of wings.

He blinked as he stared out across the gloomy ravine. He listened intently. There was a sound from somewhere over on the opposite mountain — not the piping of curlews this time, but something else. Then the shadow he had seen moving down the slope of Beinn Dearg took on a shape he recognized. It was Rooloo who, upon reaching the glen, paused by the small burn that flowed down off the cliffs behind him.

For an hour or more, he had moved down off the mountain without haste, treading quietly and with assurance. It was not until he stood by the burn and raised his head that he gave any indication that he was perturbed.

Like the eagle, he too was listening intently!

Back up the mountain, however, came no sound of pursuit. It was as quiet as only a mountain can be when the day is almost done and mist and the evening are taking possession of heights grown hoary with age. But for the frail trickling of the burn through the glen, never such a silence as this.

Rooloo felt a quiver of fear pass along his spine. All afternoon, he had been forced to keep on the move, knowing, from a stain in the wind, that stalkers were trying to locate him.

In the deep gloom of the glen, dwarfed against the immense cliffs surrounding him, Rooloo had an elfin air. He stood poised, wild creature that he was, ready to make off at the first sign of danger. His eyes, below the massive forehead crowned with its splendid antlers, were wide open and very bright. He was very frightened at the silence. His ally, the wind, seemed to have deserted him here in the glen.

His fear grew because, for the first time since he had become aware he was being hunted, he did not know where the stalkers were, although he sensed that they were probably coming down off the main ridge of Beinn Dearg.

Rooloo shifted apprehensively on his feet.

Up on the mountain, he had been more reliant. The wind had been with him, telling him exactly where the enemy was. Thus he had been able to move without haste from one point of vantage to another. Down here, in the grim acclivity of rock and bog between two mountains, he felt himself to be menaced because he had at last completely lost touch with those who had not yet given up the chase.

No longer of prime importance was the reason that had brought him down off the mountain wilderness. No longer enticing was that gap between Marsco and Beinn Dearg through which lay the pathway to the sanctuary he wished to reach. There was now, with the gloom coming swiftly down upon the mountain, and fast gathering here in the glen, the distinct possibility of a stalker already down from the hill, and with his gun trained on the gap through which Rooloo knew he must indeed go if he were to quit alive this grim and gloomy ravine of rock and burn.

The stag half turned his head as if to pierce the distance that lay between him and the open strath. He listened as, on the opposite mountain, the eagle, Greeka, was listening, for some sound from the curlews who, a moment before, had been tossing and turning over A Coire nan Brucdarun. No piping now from them. No wheeling either over the twisty burns, so it would seem. It was almost as though they had been driven away by some enemy come silently amongst them.

Even so, far over under Belig, the stag kenned that the lapwings, not yet gone for their wintering on the distant mainland shores, were rising and crying all down the winding course of the forked burn. No enemy there, he was sure; in the still of this disturbing evening, the peesweeps were still thrusting up happily into the wind, and calling out as they had always called for the last hundred years or more when the light was drained from the mountains and the green strath of the forked burn became a place of quiet isolation.

Yet, because of the fear in him, Rooloo still remained with his forefeet in the burn, his head uplifted as, with nostrils distended, he sought to catch the first trickle of air from off the mountain. Rooloo sensed that he must indeed rely upon himself if he were to leave the glen alive. Before he could make any decisive move, he must first test the wind.

Thus he waited, and on his rocky perch on Marsco, the eagle, Greeka, waited with him. The bird sensed that it was a peculiar evening.

Rooloo, however, had come once again under the protection of the Great Spirit that watched over the wild. Even though the light remained unmoving in the gap at the head of the glen, and the wind could no longer reach him in this deeply recessed hollow of rock and burn, one other was there to give him warning of danger — Greeka!

Not quite a repetition, perhaps, of that other hunt, but an eagle was there, an eagle allied with him against man.

Fear of man was common enough with all animals of the wild, and the alarm expressed by one at the appearance of the dreaded enemy was sufficient to preserve the life of another.

Thus it was with Greeka and Rooloo!

The eagle saw the movement of the first stalker to reach the floor of the glen. Following a route familiar to him, the fellow came down off the mountain by way of a water gully that had its beginnings up on Druim na Ruaige and actually terminated some hundred and fifty yards from where the stag was standing.

Rooloo had not moved. No sound had reached him, warning him of danger near at hand. The stalker, experienced in scrambling up and down water gullys and over scree slopes, had moved silently.

The very instant the hunter stepped out of the gully and stood hesitantly beside the burn, he saw the stag — a silhouette sharply drawn on that canvas of gray light that marked the eastern entrance to the glen.

His gun, strapped till then across his back, was hastily brought into position. The light was none too good, and the distance too great to ensure a successful kill. As a result, the hunter began to move forward cautiously, concentrating on keeping within cover of one or other of the many boulders that lined the bank of the burn.

"Through the heart — right through the heart it must be — " he kept saying to himself in a gasping whisper. "A wound an' he'll be away. Och! I mustn't lose him now! I canna do that. It must be a heart shot — It must — "

He trod quietly, so very quietly, a shadow amidst so many greater shadows, and he talked on to himself as if to allay some teasing doubt in his mind and still the small voice of conscience that seemed to rise up and tell him that it was an unco trick he was playing on the stag.

A hundred and fifty yards became a hundred and forty; a hundred and forty became a hundred and twenty, and a hundred and twenty less than a hundred — then scarcely more than eighty — then not more than seventy-five . . .

Still Rooloo had not moved. The trickle of wind he had been waiting for was reaching him at last, coming down from off the eastern cliffs of Beinn Dearg; and it was a cold, clean wind, with no stain in it.

Even as he tested it, with head now turned full in the direction of the gap where the last light of evening still appeared to be suspended, it seemed that the voice of the wind was stronger by far than its movement. The stag raised his head higher to test the wind and to hear its voice, leaving his neck and shoulder fully exposed. An excited look came into those very bright eyes of his. The wind was telling him clearly that the lapwings were still crying out over the forked burn.

Fifty yards away, the stalker, noting the exposed neck and shoulder of the unsuspecting stag, took up a favorable position behind an upturned rock and took sights with his gun. His hand was steady, his body perfectly balanced, despite the fact that he had one foot trailing in the burn.

His breath seemed caught up in his throat; his heart clearly missed a beat . . . Then a weird cry sounded down the entire length of the glen and a winged shape swept out from the shadows.

Both the stag and the man bent on slaying him were startled.

Even as Rooloo leaped back toward the overshadowing cliffs with a quivering cry, the stalker lost his balance as a loose stone rolled away under his knee. The gun he had held so firmly but a split second before slipped from his grasp, and the very next instant the man himself was floundering in the burn.

Greeka, more startled at the happenings on the floor of the glen, beat his way upward. As he got into the wind and started to soar, he uttered another cry. Then he went straight down the glen and over the gap.

Even as the cry went echoing through the gloomy ravine,

Rooloo swiftly turned about. Then he was away, racing madly up the narrow acclivity, approaching nearer and nearer to that gap over which the eagle had passed, and where the light was still suspended although mist was now deepening in the glen itself.

A few seconds later, the stag was through the gap — and safe! No shot disturbed the deep quietness of that ancient gully between Marsco and Beinn Dearg. The only sound the stalker heard as he stumbled out of the burn was a voice calling way up on the mountain, and when that had ceased, the heavy beating of his own heart.

As the man instinctively looked toward the gap, the last of the day withdrew — no twilight out there beyond the gap and A Coire nan Brucdarun. Only night, and a stag trotting toward a forked burn where maybe the lapwings still tossed and turned and the peesweeps called. Only night and the candles of the stars being lit one by one.

CHAPTER FIFTEEN

IN THE TRAIL OF THE
SNOW GOOSE

SHORT INDEED, THAT YEAR, WAS THE PERIOD OF THE HUNT-
ing winds. No sooner was October out, than from the north
came Kehonka, the snow goose. High over Achnasheen in
Wester Ross he flew, coming up from the direction of
Sgurr Dubh above Loch Torridon. A fisherman, sitting beside a burn at the foot of the mountain, Moruisg, saw the
goose come up out of the darkening twilight, his long neck
outstretched and his huge wings moving in perfect rhythm as
he flew a straight course.

Within a second or two of the fisherman's raising his head
from contemplation of the burn and the badly spliced rod he
held, he saw the bird vanishing swiftly into the dusk, and
heard, like an echo, the harsh cry the goose gave as he followed the north wind.

At the instant when the goose disappeared, another bird
swept up on the wind — Vigur, the great sea eagle — who
hung motionless for a second or two over the fisherman and
the burn. Then he too vanished as if seeking the lone snow
goose. Less than half a minute later, something cold and

Glen Sligachan encountered the slopes of Ruadh Stac, leaped complaining up the snow-covered scree, and escaping over the summit carried with it a mass of powdered crystals that hung, for a moment, over the Clach Glas corrie.

Again Greeka blinked, then spreading his pinions, launched off, flying above the earth-bound snow cloud. In a matter of seconds, he was carefully surveying the glen of the Sligachan River.

There was no sign of life anywhere. The snow lay unsullied and unbroken as far as the eye could see.

Swinging sideways to the wind, the eagle soared, finally passing over the Pinnacle Ridge of Sgurr nan Gillean and heading in the direction of Coire Gaisteach. North of the burn, on the fine hill of Beinn Bhreac, Greeka discovered a deep hollow where the snow was thinly scattered.

He sailed around in lazy circles, his pinions set against the wind, his fierce, keen eyes searching for possible prey. At last he was rewarded. He saw the sudden, quick movement of a rabbit.

Greeka steadied himself in the air currents, and slightly plumed his tail feathers.

The rabbit hopped a few paces, then paused. Unaware of the eagle high above him, he betrayed no sign of fear and began to crop the grass which, protected by an outcrop of rock, was only finely sprinkled with snow.

Greeka was practically motionless. Suddenly he swung around until he was headlong to the wind. The very sudden-

ness of the turn bent back the primaries of his wing tips.
Moreover, his change of position took him to a somewhat
higher level, and he was thus better placed for the stoop he
must make to trap the unsuspecting animal.

All at once, the rabbit sat up on its skut, the sensitive ears
having caught the faint strumming of the wind in the eagle's
feathers. Taut with apprehension, the rabbit sat listening,
his forepaws pressed tightly against his furry breast.

Then with a whoof of wings he came — the fierce hunter
of the skies — and the rabbit's world of snow with its patch
of green grass had gone. No outcry came from the stricken
creature clutched in the eagle's remorseless talons — nothing
— only the great silence of hills glistening in their mantle of
snow, only a vivid splash of color where the rabbit had been.
Nothing more. Even the sky above was deserted.

During the next few days it snowed most of the time, and
Greeka hunted in the neighborhood of Beinn Bhreac. The
fall of the ground from the east seemed protected by the upward sweep of Beinn na Gaoithe, and in all the white wilderness of the glen of silence, it was the one spot where here
and there grass was visible. It thus became a place that attracted many wild creatures driven by famine to take risks
in an effort to survive.

Greeka was therefore extremely fortunate in his hunting.
Apart from rabbits, he managed to supplement his larder
with two leverets and a stoat. The latter he discarded after

carrying it to the plucking post he had chosen less than a mile from the scene of his activities.

While Greeka was faring well, his enemy Panzeed was growing thin. The wildcat was unable to roam so far afield as the eagle, and as a result had the utmost difficulty in satisfying his voracious requirements. Most of the creatures he hunted seemed to have deserted the glen of Sligachan and the Corrie of the Hart; nor were they to be found in the narrow gullys that thrust upward between the snow-covered hills.

Panzeed, however, had known many such winters, and was accustomed to extreme hardship. Still, even he had to eat, and on the third day of the famine, driven by sheer necessity, he set off in the direction of Loch Scavaig.

An hour or so later found him indulging in a new game of patience. He was lying motionless on a large flat boulder that broke the downward flow of a fresh-water burn. At the base of the rock was a deep pool which, while being fed on the one side by the burn, was directly connected to the sea loch by a narrow channel cut over a rocky bed.

When the tide was rising — as now — it was usual for sea trout to come up the channel and rest in the pool.

Panzeed knew this, and like all members of his tribe, he waited with highly developed cunning, hoping that by so doing, he could repeat, with success, an exploit that had served him well in the past.

His breath was a skein of thinning mist that hung suspended in the cold, still atmosphere. It was not long before his whiskers were stickles of silver, and a rind of frost gathered on his muzzle. Despite the intense cold, the huge wildcat did not relax for a single moment. His eyes never left the pool, and all the time, the rising tide in the loch sent eddying currents racing up the narrow channel, and the pool deepened with the intake of both sea and burn water.

At last, with a swift racing inflow from the loch, a gray, dappled shape came wriggling toward the pool.

Panzeed did not move; the only indication that he was alive, and interested, was in the sudden narrowing of his eyes, and the slow, silent waving of his tail.

A gannet went sailing across the loch, uttered a wailing cry and disappeared. Two shags suddenly appeared, beating their way up the inlet in agitated flight. They touched down a few yards from the channel, saw Panzeed and rose again, screaming out in alarm.

Still the wildcat remained taut and still.

By this time, the fish had reached the pool, and sank for an instant to the bottom. Viewed through the shimmering clearness of the water, he seemed so unsubstantial a thing, yet, to the creature that watched, the fish meant life and sustenance.

Panzeed's tail moved more quickly as if with annoyance. His eyes now were little more than pinpricks.

A fresh inflow of water from the loch brought with it

some sea grubs. Even before the pool had taken the rising tide, the fish was busy, darting from one side to the other, leaping at the grubs and causing wide ripples to rise and break surface around the base of the boulder.

The wildcat continued to watch. He had, however, moved forward a trifle, and his forepaws hung over the edge of the rock.

Once again there came a cry from out at sea, and the gannet put in another appearance, this time flying directly toward the foreshore. The bird banked, swept around in a circle and approached close enough to cause Panzeed to raise his head for the first time.

In that same second, the fish — a small sea trout — began to rise from the bottom of the pool where he had gone after a grub. Almost by instinct, the cat glanced down and saw in the water, not only the trout, but the reflected shape of the gannet who had again swung off in the direction of the open sea.

The trout continued to rise, the dorsal fin scarcely moving as he came to the surface. While the ripple he caused was still widening into a perfect arc, Panzeed struck, his right paw skimming the water, then moving swiftly upward. In what for him had been a single movement of his tail from left to right, he had hooked the trout and it lay flapping help-lessly within an inch of his gaping jaws.

Three further fish Panzeed caught that day, and for a

short time, like Greeka, he deserted his old hunting grounds, and concentrated on catching the sea trout with an adroitness that outmatched his enemy in such matters.

The very cold spell showed no sign of breaking. There were often heavy falls of snow, generally followed by a hard frost. More than ever did the neighborhood of the mountains resemble an unexplored region of the far arctic wastes. No human being trod the trail from Sligachan; no hungry deer came down off the mountain ridge of Lord MacDonald's Forest.

The world might have been uninhabited!

During the second week of the snow, a gaggle of geese descended upon Loch Slapin on the eastern slopes of Blaven. They stayed but one night, for next morning they had gone, leaving no sign of their brief visit save for a few scrabbling marks in the snow. Yet another day saw the appearance of some wild ducks. They, however, only encircled the small tarn in Glen Sligachan and were away without attempting to alight.

Panzeed heard them calling as they flew round and round. Then, as he crouched at the mouth of the corrie watching them, they seemed to rise in a scurry of brown and red and green, and the next moment the sky was empty of all else save a fluttering of snow which had come with the turn of the evening wind.

That month too was the month when most of the salmon die. Those that had not yet reached the sea were already dead or dying in the reaches of the ocean-going rivers. The inevitable law — undisputable, undefeatable — worked in this year of snow as ruthlessly as it had in former years when only rain swept the mountains. Salmon of five or six spawning seasons, salmon of only a single season — all were dying, weakened by the efforts they had made at spawning time, yet all endeavoring to reach the great mother of all fish — the sea! Perhaps in the midst of so much waste, only the river knew why, year after year, its finest fish must die before reaching the cleansing, life-giving sea.

The violent shedding of spawn and milt by the salmon would, in due time, bring back life where life was now passing. Already in the spawning beds of the higher reaches of the rivers the recurring miracle was starting. What one day would be young grilse, and later, fine, silver-garbed salmon, was quickening beneath the gravel. Life was a spontaneous, never-ending thing.

In the rivers, it had ever been thus.

However, because salmon were dying in this bitter month of cold, and famine existed in the wilderness, Greeka was introduced to a change of diet. It came about when he followed a mountain burn down to the Drynoch River at the head of Loch Harport. He had just swung effortlessly over Beinn Bhreac and encircled the tarn known as Lochan a Ghrobain when he saw, in the slow-going tide of the river, a glint of something leaping. The eagle immediately slipped into a downward glide and followed the winding course of the river. Then, at a point where it sped over shallows broken with stones and boulders, he saw once again the glint that had brought him off his usual route.

Three spawned-out salmon, almost dead, were making a last frantic effort to get downstream to the loch, and from thence to the sea where the life-giving water would mayhap cleanse and make them whole. They showed at first over the edge of a small pool that lay upstream from the shallows. Dorsal and caudal fins broke the still surface of the pool as, time and time again, all three endeavored to bring up sufficient reserves of strength to attempt passage over the shallows.

As Greeka thrust up into the sky to make another glide over the river, there was one other bird high above him also watching the salmon. It was Vigur, the sea eagle recently come in the wake of the snow goose from the far-off mountains of Dranga Jokull.

Vigur was more knowledgeable than Greeka in the art of taking salmon from a pool, and even as the young bird thrust upward to attain an altitude beneficial for an easy glide over the river, the sea eagle went into a stoop. His keen eye had seen one of the salmon rising in the pool, and he knew at once that a leap was imminent.

There was a sudden thundering beat of powerful wings sounding over the winding course of the Drynoch River, the lightning-like glint of a salmon leaping up out of the splintered mirror of the pool. The next instant, pool and salmon were momentarily blotted out as Vigur struck, then soared rapidly with the salmon held in a clutch that was both relentless and death-dealing.

The immense bird's timing had been perfect!

Greeka had scarcely made his turn high over Loch a Ghrobain when he beheld Vigur soaring upward with the salmon held securely in the right foot. Just one short, fleeting glimpse Greeka had of the sea eagle — a glimpse that was no more than the passing of a silent, wheeling shadow. Then Vigur had vanished as Greeka went gliding downward on a favorable current of air.

Only a harsh cry, fading away into the sunless sky, proclaimed that the greatest hunter of the eagle clan had made a kill.

By this time, one of the remaining two salmon had started threshing its way around the pool, feeling no doubt that the safest place lay in the swift run of water beyond the shallows. The other, spurred on by the example of its companion, also took a quick turn around the pool.

Then, as Greeka came gliding high above the watercourse, both, almost simultaneously, attempted the fatal leap. As fatal indeed for them as it had been for their companion that Vigur had caught in the split second of his leaping. They were not, however, swooped upon by the eagle who was floating so leisurely above them, but through lack of strength fell in the very center of the shallows, half in and half out of the trickle of water that slipped, almost soundlessly, over the pebbles toward the larger stream that would have enabled them to reach the loch and the sea.

More than a dozen times did Greeka thrust up and turn, only to glide back along the river to pass once more the spot where the two salmon were lying. On each occasion as Greeka passed on downstream, he noticed that less perceptible became the movements of the stranded fish. At last he saw that they were very still, their strength spent, and the thin trickle of water just lapping their fins as it slipped by.

Finally, Greeka made a wide sweep above the spot, turned in the wind and glided down, alighting gently on a rock that was within a few inches of the now dead salmon.

Each was at least seven pounds in weight, and since it was impossible for the young eagle to perform the feat of Vigur who, apart from being the larger bird, had taken his salmon while still on the wing, Greeka settled down to feast on the fish where they lay.

In such a manner then did Greeka, the golden eagle, follow the example of Vigur and become a fisheater and with less effort than in the case of his enemy, Panzeed.

It was that same evening after he had stripped the salmon, leaving only fins and bones, that he encountered the wildcat who was making for his lair. Because the day was fast dying over the hills, and the eagle could make no just claim to being a nocturnal bird of prey, Greeka was making for his eyrie by flying direct across the main Cuillin ridge. Dark though it had become, the bird yet saw the movement of the cat as, crossing over Bidein, he swung headlong into the air currents of Harta Corrie.

Panzeed was loping leisurely when the eagle came up out of the gloom — a dark, wide-pinioned shadow. The cat let out a scream of fear as the shape came diving down upon him. He sprang to one side, his jaws gaping, his claws fully extended.

Greeka, however, was at a disadvantage in the now rapidly darkening corrie. As Panzeed flung himself out of reach of the eagle's talons, the bird himself began to rise, and before the cat had overcome his spasm of fear, Greeka had gone, and the corrie was full of shadows that deepened over the pockets of snow.

Panzeed moved less confidently to his lair under the stone when once again he made off. He was frightened. Greeka was fast becoming an obsession.

When he finally lay curled up with his nose tucked into his tail, he dreamed dark dreams, and in them he had avenged himself, and Greeka — the winged shape he feared — was no more.

The hour of reckoning was surely not far off!

CHAPTER SIXTEEN

THE EAGLE FROM GLEN TORRIDON

IN A FEW WEEKS, SPRING, QUITE SUDDENLY, BEGAN TO MAKE
timid overtures to offset the ravages of winter. The snow soon
disappeared from the moors, leaving in the glens stretches
of bogland, and burns that flowed freely with floodwater. On
the mountain ridges, however, the snow hardened into ice,
and it would take many weeks of rising temperatures to dis-
perse the heavy pockets that lay between the peaks.

Life was stirring once more. The heather began to glow
with a fresh display of vigor; the larches, planted by the
Forestry Commission above Glen Brittle, pushed forth new
spearheads of gold as if to defy the ice pinnacles ranged in
opposition across the valley.

In the sea-going rivers, salmon were once again putting
in an appearance, fine, healthy fish, all agleam with silver
and threshing the downward-flowing water with a great show
of vitality.

As always, in the turn of the year, life reasserted itself, and
curlews, silent for the past few months, called again over the
moors, herons from across the lochs —

During one of these first days of approaching spring,

Greeka had a further encounter with the sea eagle, Vigur. There was a half gale blowing at the time, and Greeka was enjoying a period of soaring in favorable currents of air. Master of the wind, he kept turning and turning, lifting himself with ease as a surge of air came at him with a touch of fury in its bite.

Fully three thousand feet above him, with wings curved slightly backward, hung the immense sea eagle, also complete master of the wind and enjoying as much as Greeka the tremendous surges of air that thrummed in his fanned-out tail feathers. In the secret tides of space was he fixed, riding the currents like a ship at anchor, his eyes shining fiercely, his curved beak, as yellow as his feet, pointing downward.

Greeka had scarcely risen a further thousand feet when Vigur saw a mallard rising suddenly from off the small lochan of na Sguabaidh in the region of Strath Mor. He tilted himself a little in the wind the better to watch the mallard's progress up the strath.

The mallard began to rise, beating upward over Glas Bheinn Mhor until he was almost four hundred feet above the summit.

Then, as Greeka suddenly became aware of the sea eagle high above him, Vigur keeled over, and slipped down the air lanes of the sky in a slanting line. Straight for the mallard he flew, a brownish-gray shape with pinions like daggers cleaving the wind.

Greeka had no sooner balanced himself in an air pocket to watch Vigur's assault on the mallard when the small bird became conscious of the sea eagle hurtling down upon him. He made a valiant effort to reach the security of Loch Ainort, was indeed planing down toward the upper reaches when Vigur overtook him.

The eagle struck with his claw, severing the mallard's head from its body, and with his striking, Vigur went racing past his now headless victim. A second later he had flattened out and doubling back up the air lanes, caught and bound securely in his clutch the falling body of the mallard as he soared.

Up and up he went, passing the level at which Greeka hung watching him, up still higher until he passed through a mass of cloud and vanished.

No cry from him this time to give notice of his departure from the scene of his hunting, only the cloud riven by the passing through it of his powerful shape, riven so badly that it started to thin out and fly on the wind in tattered streamers of mist.

Beyond the thinning cloud, no sign of Vigur now; he had vanished completely!

It was on that same day that Greeka began to experience the old, recurring restlessness of his tribe. At first it was manifest in the sudden loneliness he felt when he witnessed Vigur sweeping upward through the cloud, then in his brooding on his rocky ledge on Clach Glas. Eventually, he found himself possessed with a strange longing to travel great distances, and reacting on it, flew high over Bealach Mor, his old home.

The eyrie on Roineval no longer attracted him. It was already being prepared by Groonah and Greesha for the new brood they hoped to rear when spring was well on its way.

High though he was over his old haunts, Greeka knew well that the nest was being replenished with new sprigs of heather. As he banked toward Beinn Totaig, he saw Groonah flying in with some fresh cuttings in her beak.

With the passing days, Greeka's restlessness grew. Mornings there were when he was awake on his ledge long before the sun came up — an unusual thing, for eagles are notoriously late risers.

Meanwhile, the northern hemisphere was turning more and more toward the sun. While for a week or so, the mornings continued dark, the evenings were unquestionably drawing out. The new moon that month came in with the western wind, a mere sickle of silver dimmed by sudden rain. This gentler wind did not carry the cold, sharp lashes of the north wind, nor did it bring ice and snow.

One evening, as Greeka came back to his nest on the Clach Glas ridge, far over, beyond the tableland of the Trotternish, was a long line of cloud that bore a close resemblance to a vast continent risen up from out of the sea. The whole bank of vapor was purple in the dusk, but when the stars came out, they shone large and bright over the gathering storm which, when darkness fell, suddenly broke up and returned to the sea from whence it came.

That night was calm and quiet, but very cold, with millions of stars in bright array, and the moon, in its first quarter, going down into the western ocean like a boat slipping out on a long voyage.

Next day, the great call came to Greeka!

Dawn broke with a hint of the splendid hours that were to follow. Like the kindling of a gigantic furnace in the east, the sun smoldered and finally leaped into flame. Along the whole of the horizon it gathered in ever-changing colors that set the entire heavens aquiver. The last of the stars grew pale and lost beauty in the van of that swift-rising dawn.

While Greeka preened his breast feathers, sitting on the edge of his nesting place, the colorful sunrise began to clothe the mountains with a raiment of many hues, taking away from the peaks a little of their rugged appearance.

Even at that early hour, the larks began to rise from the moorland and scattered abroad their staccato songs that rose, like sharp-edged arrows, in the clear light of an almost cloudless sky. Stonechats set about their earnest building under the mountain stones; the full-voiced ewes repeatedly called their errant young. There was also the soft calling note of the buzzard from across the moors above Camasunary; the persistent murmur of the mountain burns that tumbled, ice-cold, like torrents of fine-cut jewels, into the green glens that washed the flanks of the imperishable hills.

The mists departed; the rolling stretches of the moorland seemed to quicken in luxurious splendor to greet the rising sun and the fine beginning of a perfect spring morning.

Greeka was acutely conscious of the stirring of life on the moors and up in the hills. The restlessness that had been upon him these many days was now like a warm stream that brought new life to his quivering members, and a great strength to those pinions he sensed he would spread that morning on the long journey he must make. So strong indeed was the flow of that stream in his veins that he did not experience hunger — only the subtle urging to be away — to rise over the peaks he now knew as home.

It was not, however, till he saw the female bird fly off across the corrie and then suddenly return with a root of heather in her beak, that he sensed he must find himself a mate. The instant that overwhelming realization thrust itself upon him, he knew why he must be away, why, too, he must make a long journey.

As with all his tribe, he must seek for himself a mate from some distant glen.

Before his neighbor had reached her nesting place where the male bird still slept with his head sunk deep in his feathers, Greeka, the lone eagle, was fluttering his wings in readiness to be off.

The southwest wind, coming up the glen and leaping

up the corrie, called to Greeka as it swept past his ledge on Clach Glas. "Come with me," it seemed to say. "Follow me across the sea to the mountains of the north. There you will find what you seek!"

In a continuous stream, the wind flew unabated past the ramparts of the mountain, and always it said the same thing, "Come away with me," and Greeka, the lone eagle of the Hebrides, at last obeyed.

It required no special effort to reach a high altitude that morning. The eagle rose straight above the corrie without a single wingbeat. He spiraled rapidly until Blaven and Clach Glas were just rocky ridges rising with the rest of the Cuillin range out of the green strath of the Sligachan River.

When at the height of some four thousand feet, Greeka made a slow and graceful turn before setting his course with the wind. His keen eyes glanced down at the world below. He could see every movement with exceptional clearness. Then he swung into the wind, heading north.

Down in Harta Corrie, Panzeed loped back to his lair after a night of illegal hunting — the torn remains of a lamb being evidence of his nocturnal activities. Up on Beinn Dearg, Rooloo, whom the eagle had saved from destruction, stood at the head of his herd as Greeka passed on his way.

He sent forth a deep belling note that echoed across the mountains, reaching the ears of the wildcat who paused for a moment, his eyes gleaming with indecision.

Before the stag's belling note had entirely gone from

the mountains, Panzeed had disappeared into his lair, and Greeka, his enemy, was crossing the sea that kept Skye from the mainland.

The eagle's greatest adventure was about to begin!

The Isle of Scalpay lay directly below, with the greater Isle of Raasay on his left wing tip. In a matter of moments — short in the long life that was to be his — he had passed over the Crowlin Islands, and directly ahead was the mainland of Wester Ross. There were numerous small lakes gleaming in the sunlight, with high, precipitous mountains rising up around the deer forests of Applecross.

When he sensed that here, perhaps, his journey was to end, the wind seemed to tell him that these were not the hills he sought. He continued on, gliding with ease along the pathways of the air. The ground was a map of many colors, broken with mountains and deep valleys, with many small lakes, and then once again the sea which was Loch Torridon.

At the height he was flying, Greeka could see an immense distance. His gaze, however, suddenly became concentrated on the wild district of mountain now directly below him, with the wide stretch of Loch Maree engirdling it in the extreme north.

Here the wind began to lessen and seemed to be veering toward the vast mountain wastes on the northern slopes of Glen Torridon.

Almost without effort, Greeka followed the gradual turn of the wind, and as a result, commenced to encircle the scarred flanks of the mountains, Beinn Alligin, the Wester Ross Beinn Dearg, and the massive bulk of the Beinn Eighe and Liathach group. This wide sweep he made, still following the spin of the wind, brought him to the upper reaches of Glen Torridon, with the whole range of the Torridon Mountains now on his right wing tip.

The wind had become a mere trickle of air. No longer did it cry to Greeka to follow it. Instead, its voice had become a soft whisper repeating "Here, here!" Obedient to the entreaty, the eagle banked, dropped in altitude and finally planed down toward Coire Mhic Fhearchair with its small lochan surrounded with innumerable peaks.

Gliding gently, the bird came to rest on a spur of rock, his head turning from left to right as he surveyed the wild inner fastnesses of Beinn Eighe. He was entirely at home in such grim surroundings. The old familiar sounds were also here to greet him — the roar of water somewhere in the corrie — the faint calling of a buzzard and, coming from a gully he could not see, the unmistakable bark of one of his own tribe.

This sound, rising above the others, quickened his interest and brought a keener gleam to his already keen eyes. He knew at once that the call came from a female of his species. The journey he had made at the behest of the wind was for this alone — to end his existence as a lone bird, and to return to his ledge on Clach Glas with the mate who would remain with him for the rest of his life. Moreover, as he sat there on the spur of rock, he knew that he was being observed, and that the female had seen him the instant he planed down over the corrie. As was the habit of the Falconidae, he, the male, awaited some overt move on the part of the female.

In those few short minutes that he sat waiting and listening, the wind drifted quietly across the small tarn and caused tiny waves to ruffle the mirrorlike surface. When the wind had ceased to blow and the water was again still, once more Greeka heard the call of the female.

He knew now exactly where she was. She had taken up a new position in the deep cleft that broke the face of the second and third peaks of Beinn Eighe. Below the cleft, the scree was still white with snow, and Greeka, sitting with his head pointing across the small lochan, was aware that he could mark at once any short flight she might make.

For a long time he sat unmoving, conscious of the roar of falling water and the far-off calling of the buzzard. Suddenly he too gave a gruff bark, raising high his head in an effort to send the note clearly across the tarn. The sound had scarcely left his throat when a golden-brown shape swept across the snowy scree, made a swift turn over the water, then thrust up into the air currents that came off the summit of the mountain.

Immediately, Greeka left the spur of rock and was flying

quickly over the tarn, sweeping upward in an ecstasy of excitement. No sound did either of the birds utter. Their first amorous advances demanded complete silence.

In all that world of the lochan and the surrounding mountain peaks, only one sound was heard — the muffled voice of the distant fall of water. Before Greeka had risen above the summit ridge of Beinn Eighe, even that was no longer audible. Then, as he found the air streams, coming more clearly to him now was the repeated crying of the buzzard, also seeking a mate.

Greeka, sailing easily on outspread pinions, could see the female eagle spiraling up and up. Then, having apparently reached an exceptionally strong current of air, she started to drift over the mountain, moving faster and faster.

Greeka followed, until he also was caught up in that same strong flow of wind which carried him high over Loch Clair on the opposite side of the range. There — over the wide reaches of the loch — both birds thrust up at each other in play. Now, like a symphony, the breeze sang in the larch forest that fringed the lower flanks of Sgurr Dubh on the western shore, until the voice of the buzzard was lost in that greater surging of music from the trees so plaintively responsive to the subtle fingers of Nature herself.

So began the days of Greeka's courtship in the Torridon Mountains.

CHAPTER SEVENTEEN

THE DUEL IN THE CORRIE OF THE HART

NEVER BEFORE HAD THERE BEEN KNOWN SUCH A SPRING IN the Western Highlands. While winter still held sovereignty on the mountain peaks, and snow sometimes came on a drift of wind from the north, spring, still seeming shy and timid, nevertheless continued its overtures. In sheltered hollows wild flowers put in an appearance; new growth of rushes bordering the tarns and lochans came shooting forth like lances guarding the solitary shores. More persistent now were the voices of the stonechats, more keenly tuned the songs of the larks. Grouse called hoarsely as springtime heralded the days of rebirth; salmon leaping in the rivers were full of health and vigor, and the rivers were themselves part of the new life that stirred in them.

In this rebirth of the world, Greeka, the golden eagle from Clach Glas, played and soared into the cloud-dappled arc of heaven with Gruilma, his mate who dwelled on Beinn Eighe.

Meanwhile, in Harta Corrie, Panzeed, the wildcat with

no mate, was making for himself a never-ending chain that
would ultimately bring about his destruction.

Panzeed, following the days of famine, had developed a
taste for mutton, and scarcely a night went by but what
he claimed one of the small lambs from a flock of mountain
sheep which grazed on the lower moors at the foot of Sgurr
nan Gillean.

Their shepherd began to keep special watch, and one
morning, just as dawn was breaking, saw the wildcat making
his way back to Harta Corrie. Investigation of the ground
near which another lamb had been ravaged disclosed the
cat's paw marks. While he was still examining the impressions, he saw some sheep which had strayed farther up
the glen suddenly scatter with bleating cries of fear. He
knew it was because they had seen the cat making for his
lair.

When an hour later the shepherd set off for his small
croft, he knew that, at all costs, his flock had to be safeguarded
against such attacks, and there was only one way to do it.
He would have to set a trap for the attacker!

Thus, as the spring of that year turned more and more
toward the hour of its fulfilment, the fate of Panzeed was determined. Although he was not to die in the jaws of a steel
trap as the shepherd planned, the threads of his destiny became caught up in another fateful pattern such as had, in
an earlier spring, taken Tawny-eye. With those fine-drawn

threads were also entwined those of Greeka and the mate with whom he still frolicked in the glen below the far Torridon Mountains.

Indeed, in this spring of an early Hebridean summer, the wheel of life began to spin with increasing velocity, each turn bringing into its orbit all who had known the eagle, Greeka.

Out of small, seemingly unrelated, incidents started to emerge the final design of an intricate tracery. Soon would it be unfolded under the lee of those frowning cliffs, where the mists gathered before quiet dawns, and the tumbling burns sang their changeless melody born out of some strange mountain fantasy.

Meanwhile, the spring continued to grow in splendor over the mountains. The remaining snow started to melt away and the moment for the return of the snow goose to the arctic north was imminent. Imminent, too, was the violent departure of Panzeed from the haunts which had known him for so long.

The shepherd who had planned Panzeed's destruction trudged up Glen Sligachan toward Harta Corrie. Under one arm he carried a springtrap.

It was a lovely evening — that evening of his journey up the glen. The sun was going down in a sky of amethyst and pearl. The light on the mountain peaks was as clear as crystal.

As the shepherd turned to go up the corrie, overhead passed two eagles making for the ledge on Clach Glas.

Greeka had returned with his mate, Gruilma!

The light was long a-dying on the mountains. When at last it had gone, the stars shone with all the brilliancy of magical lamps marking the way to the vast hunting grounds that lay in the fields of eternity.

Although an old saying in the Hebrides indicated that the face of early spring was a foretaste of the summer that was to come — "like the movement of a budding poplar on the edge of a sea-blue sky". . . winter did not always relinquish its grip without a struggle. An hour or so before dawn on that fateful day in the lives of Greeka and Panzeed, the stars in the north were blotted out by a trailing garment of cloud. Then the north wind itself came up suddenly, almost like a defeated enemy fighting a delaying retreat. From the cloud it took the last few weapons that remained, and for a short while, Skye was attacked with a violent squall of hail.

The wind made its first onslaught in the neighborhood of the Trotternish. Then driving onward with greater fury, it swept down on Bealach Mor, shouted with defiance over the rocky crags of Roineval, where Greesha and Groonah slept on the new nest they had prepared on the site of the old.

It passed at last from the Trotternish glen; passed too from

Bealach Mor and Roineval and went scudding across Loch Harport and the mid-Carbost heights to vent its weakening fury upon the relentless crags of the Black Cuillins.

Even as it withdrew from the region of the Trotternish, with the sky over by Talisker still bright with stars, beyond Preshal Mor in the east, there was already a faint ripple of light as if dawn was stirring and the night preparing for its retreat westward.

In no time, it seemed, the hail had passed over; the northern stars were out again, while the new day gathered strength and flamed beyond the mountains on the mainland.

No sign of the storm was evident in Harta Corrie when Panzeed, after another night of illegal hunting, returned tired and sluggish from the meal he had made just as the sun came up.

The wildcat passed, all unsuspecting, the steel-toothed implement that had been set for his destruction. Sgurr nan Gillean was reflected in the still waters of the tarn in the glen. Nothing moved there. Even the tussocks of bog grass were still. No movement either was there under the huge red boulder around which, according to legend, was fought a fierce battle between the MacDonalds and the MacLeods. The springtrap set beneath the boulder was exactly as the shepherd had left it. Due to the fact that two days before the cat had trapped a rabbit close to the stone, and had left imprints on the soft ground, the old crofter had thought the lair to be in the hollow beneath the legendary relic.

As Panzeed went down into his cavern some distance from the red boulder, up over the northern flank of Druim nan Ramh a sea bird wheeled white in the sunlight before disappearing behind the splintered screes of Lota Coire.

About the same time, the shepherd who had intended going up the glen to ascertain whether or not his plan had succeeded was visited by a neighbor who required assistance in repairing the roof of his croft. The old shepherd, confident that any creature caught in the trap would be killed instantly, saw no reason why he should go immediately to the corrie, and accordingly delayed his journey until the evening.

Thus was woven the final thread necessary to complete the pattern that Time itself had spun.

Gruilma was awake early that morning. While Greeka still slept, she looked out across the corrie, reviewing with appraising eye the surroundings which, in future, were to be her hunting grounds.

She was well satisfied with what she saw. It was indeed a wild spot Greeka had chosen. The nest, too, was ideally placed, for viewed from the angle at which she surveyed it, the corrie rose practically sheer from the glen below, and although the sun was up, its rays had not yet brought light to the gloomy grandeur of Clach Glas.

When she finally moved toward the edge of the eyrie, Gruilma saw the cliffs falling away, scarred by the countless storms that, in bygone years, had torn shrieking through the glen. She, herself, could not have found a better nesting site on Beinn Eighe.

With a sharp, piercing look, she turned toward Greeka and gave a low, clear call.

He awakened at once. Gruilma then fluttered her pinions, and flinging herself from the ledge, started to flap off down the glen, keeping close to the scree-strewn slopes of Ruadh Stac.

Greeka followed immediately, and soon both were quartering the moorland in the vicinity of the Sligachan River.

Rabbits were numerous that morning, and the sun had been scarcely two hours above the horizon before they had feasted well. Then, while Greeka stood on a small boulder digesting his meal, Gruilma flew around in ever-widening circles. Suddenly she saw a cliff edge that attracted her, and flew straight toward it.

Her glide along the face of the cliff was slow and restrained until she caught sight of a green plateau. In a trice she had turned. The small plateau was just below the ridge known to mountaineers as Nead na h'Iolaire — the nest of the eagle.

Without hesitation, Gruilma settled on the mossy spot — the only green place on the whole of that grim rock ledge. There, with her head tilted at an excited angle, she stared out across the glen as, more than a hundred years before, her own parents had stood and gazed.

Gruilma's attraction for the "nest of the eagle" was not without significance. As she was standing now, looking out over Glen Sligachan, so would she stand for long hours at a stretch during the months that lay ahead. So too would she be standing one gray afternoon in the fall when the mountains would be steaming with mist, and he whom she sought came gliding up the winding course of the Sligachan River.

No presentiment, however, had she as she stood, looking out over the glen which had been such a familiar sight to those from whom she had sprung.

All she knew on that fine spring morning was that she was happy with her mate!

For the rest of that day, Greeka and Gruilma alternatively hunted the glens and soared high over the riven corries of the Cuillin Mountains. Times there were when it seemed they were chasing the swift-moving shadows up the lochs below; times also when they appeared to be thrusting upward into the very heart of the sky where clouds drifted on the current of the wind.

The sun was swinging down in the west when both birds finally flew over the main ridge and came sailing over the already darkening Corrie of the Hart.

Panzeed was abroad early that evening, moving up toward the red boulder with short, easy strides. There was a certain arrogance about him as he loped along with his sinuous body low to the ground.

The instant Greeka saw the wildcat, he dropped low, and

came drifting down between the cliffs of the corrie on motionless pinions.

Silent though his approach was, Panzeed was yet aware of his presence and made at once for the security of the boulder, passing within a couple of feet of the concealed springtrap. Arching his back, he stood close against the rock with one paw raised, ready to strike down the eagle should he attempt an assault.

Unfortunately for Greeka, because he now had a mate to protect, he experienced the urgent desire to defeat the wildcat. While Gruilma made a short encircling flight over the arena, Greeka hovered for a moment, came to within a few feet of the red boulder, then dropped.

Panzeed spat angrily and made a savage upward thrust with his paw.

Greeka was too quick for him. He keeled over and went drifting downwind, only to return suddenly, less than four feet from the ground.

Again Panzeed made a swift upward thrust with his paw, and this time, to avoid it, the eagle half lifted himself and fell back a pace or two. He instantly encountered the springtrap. In the very moment that he felt the jaws move beneath his tail feathers, he essayed to lift himself. Too late, however, for with a sharp metallic snap, the jaws closed and Greeka was held captive by one talon.

The fear that comes to all trapped creatures came to him then. Even his dreaded enemy was forgotten in the panic that drove him fluttering forward. This action startled Panzeed more than the sudden metallic sound had done, and he leaped for the top of the boulder.

The sight of the cat's leap brought even greater panic to the eagle. His huge pinions beat the air, but he was powerless to lift himself. The more he struggled, the greater became the frenzy within him, cumulating in a rising tide of pain that seemed to leave his foot and run like fire through his whole body.

Meanwhile, Gruilma had come in low to her mate's assistance. The wildcat was completely unaware that she was almost on him. Snarling, he prepared to leap on Greeka's back and tear him to pieces.

Panzeed had all but made the leap when Gruilma swooped. Her outstretched talons struck as the cat's arched back lent strength to his legs. A piercing scream came from him as Gruilma's grip sank deep into his flesh. In an extremity of terror, he tried to turn, heard Greeka still beating the air in vain, heard for the last time the distant belling of a stag.

Then everything became lost to him, for Gruilma's grip tightened, one talon piercing the wildcat's heart. His legs kicked convulsively, his claws becoming broken on the boulder as in his dying moment he dug deeply as if to retain a hold on life. Then his body went limp, and Panzeed's wild, lawless spirit was away to those greater hunting grounds beyond the stars.

When some fifteen minutes later the old shepherd came

up the corrie with a sack slung over his shoulder, he saw the body of the cat lying some distance from the stone, saw an eagle held by its foot in the trap he had set, and another — a larger, fiercer bird — rising swiftly as he appeared.

When speaking of the incident some weeks later, he said that when the female eagle passed overhead, the whole corrie seemed darkened by her enormous wing span.

It was as though night had come suddenly down to hide from his eyes the bird that lay struggling in the trap beneath the red boulder.

CHAPTER EIGHTEEN

NO MORE THE WILD WINGS SOUNDING

IT WAS INDEED NO EXAGGERATION WHEN THE OLD SHEPHERD said that the whole of the Corrie of the Hart had been darkened by the female bird's wing span as she rose at his approach from the place on the red boulder where she had been keeping watch over her stricken mate. He must have been a man to whom speech did not come freely, for never a mention did he make of that same shadow following him down the length of the Sligachan glen as he made his way slowly and laboriously toward the lodge of the tenant of the Deer Estate. No mention either did he make of the crow, black as soot, who came flying across the strath and then doubled back the way he had come at sight of the huge bird of prey, floating on the wind currents directly over the strange human figure hunched under the sack he carried.

He was indeed a man of few words if he did not mention this episode of the crow, for he had paused on the brink of a burn to watch Gruilma suddenly go into the attack before the soot-black bird could reach safety. Magnificent too that stoop Gruilma made on the unfortunate crow. Even Vigur, the sea eagle, could not have bettered it, for like him, she slew the crow with one mighty blow, then, not troubling to retrieve his broken body, she turned swiftly, effortlessly, to take up once again her position in the air streams above the old shepherd.

The old man had a feeling that perhaps he had acted unwisely in thrusting the eagle into the sack which he had intended for the body of Panzeed. Yet — and this question he continually asked himself as he trudged along, glancing up apprehensively at Gruilma so persistently following him. What else could he have done, for the eagle had badly damaged his primaries in endeavoring to escape from the trap? Moreover, the injured foot would prevent him from hunting even had it been possible for him to fly.

Thus argued the shepherd as mile after mile he trudged up the glen, with the Sligachan River gleaming silver-white in the late afternoon light, and the mountains close massed on the very edge of the strath.

He was reassured by the tenant of the Deer Forest when she saw the state of the bird. She said he had done quite right in bringing the eagle to her. The bird was put in a barred enclosure, once a kennel for deerhounds.

Greeka squatted disconsolately in one corner of the enclosure as the spring day went fading over the dark continent of the clouds that lay low down in the western sky. He did not know that way over above Glamaig, Gruilma slowly turned in the air lanes, keeping the white lodge under constant surveillance until the approaching twilight warned her that she must seek out a resting place for the night.

Thus, before gloom had shrouded the mountains, she flew around the southern flank of Glamaig and took up a position on the grassy plateau she had discovered that very morning on Sgurr nan Gillean. From it, when a new day came moving silently up the glen, she would be able to see clearly up the narrow strath between Glamaig and the mountain, Marsco. The white lodge where Greeka was captive would be visible to her keen eyes.

Once settled on the plateau, with the whole of Glen Sligachan but a wing's thrust away, time seemed to drag, and slow in passing seemed the last of that fateful day. As on another occasion, when the hunting winds were loose upon the hills and a stag stood in a rocky acclivity waiting to escape through a gap between the cliffs to safety, so now did the gray light of day seem merely to withdraw a little up the glen and remain unmoving where night should surely have been encamped.

Gruilma grumbled audibly and ruffled her wings.

The Sligachan River seemed transparent as did the two small lochans way over by Ruadh Stac. Only a few sheep moved along the flank of the mountain and by the winding course of the river — sheep who would never more be menaced by Panzeed. A curlew, late abroad, continually kept up a plaintive whistling; then the stag which Greeka had helped to preserve belled from his isolation on Beinn Dearg, the note peeling down off the mountain like a prolonged bugle note, bringing to the garrison of the wild, the rally to sleep.

Gruilma grumbled once again and stared out across the glen.

A few drops of wind-scattered rain fell; a blob of cotton grass on the edge of the plateau waved as if with disapproval at the brooding bird until it was borne outward in the direction of the glen where the rain-moistened fingers of the wind plucked it from the stalk and sent it wandering into the shadows like a bodiless mountain sprite that might never again know a safe anchorage.

Another sharp scud of rain came over the ridge, and before it had ceased, the last of the day no longer stood withdrawn in the glen, but went quickly. Even as the last belling note from the stag came echoing off the summit of Beinn Dearg, so did the first loud drumbeats of the west wind sound up on the crags of Sgurr nan Gillean, and it was night at last!

Such a lonely night it was for Gruilma. She could not sleep. A final drift of rain passed off quickly with the drumbeats of the wind sounding their last tattoo way over on Glamaig, and at midnight, the sky was bright with a million, million stars which shone down not only on Gruilma, but also on Greeka imprisoned in that barred enclosure which had once housed hounds trained for the hunt.

Dawn came at last — a rampant, fiery dawn, blazing and spreading all over the eastern horizon. Not for long had it

been flaring before Gruilma stirred herself, and was away
from the plateau and quartering the glen adjacent to the river
where she trapped a rabbit.

No thought had she at all for her own hunger. No sooner
had she made the kill than she was soaring rapidly, and made
with all haste to the white lodge and the enclosure where
Greeka sat staring unblinking at the dawn.

Gruilma made a sharp turn when directly over the building, then planed down to alight silently on the roof of the
enclosure, the rabbit held in one foot.

Her mate roused himself as he heard the faint whoof of
her wings. He looked up. For an instant only did he look,
then mad with delight tried to beat his way free. More of
his splendid feathers were broken in his assault on his prison.
Gruilma too was roused to a pitch of excitement at the efforts
he made.

She felt an obscure resentment that he should be unable
to reach her. As Greeka stopped his futile threshing against
the bars, she felt the morning wind sweeping around her
with exceptional gentleness, and she gave a soft call to her
mate — so much a call of distress that he started once again
to beat against the bars of his prison —

So fierce was the struggle he waged that he attracted the
attention of the old sheep dog who slept in one of the out-
houses. As the animal came racing out, Gruilma glided away,
turning slowly in the wind that was still sweeping around her
with an indescribable softness of touch.

For most of the hours of that day, she kept within ranging distance of the lodge, often passing high overhead and uttering a low-pitched call to her mate below.

Only toward evening did she turn away from that white building set hard against the old stalker's road and almost within the very shadow of the conical shape of Glamaig. There was a decided touch of coldness in the air stream she followed — a coldness like the last trace of winter that still lurked in snow pockets on the mountain.

Moving swiftly, she passed down the run of the wind and prepared to hunt in the nearby salt marshes above Loch Sligachan.

There were a few wild geese and a couple of redshanks. The geese were, for the most part, scattered close to the water's edge. One, however, was well up the pebbly beach, and by the way he dragged a wing, it was clear that he was injured.

Gruilma took little notice of him. She was not interested in the geese nor the redshanks.

Just above the head of the loch was some rough pastureland, and even from the altitude at which she approached it she had yet glimpsed the many rabbit tracks that intersected it, tracks moreover that were smooth from recent usage.

She encircled the spot and keeled over. As she did so, a few more geese came flying in low up the loch, battling laboriously against a sea-going wind. They gave a honking call as they turned to plane down, and those geese who were already in possession of the foreshore moved up to make room for the new arrivals.

It was then, as the eagle made another turn over the neck of the loch, that she noticed a crow worrying the injured goose. The black scavenger kept creeping up behind the bird and stabbing at him maliciously.

Gruilma thrust upward, and encountering a favorable current of air, half turned to keep the crow within her line of vision.

The sight of the black creature somehow antagonized her. The crow reminded her of how, the previous evening, when Greeka was being carried up the glen in a sack to captivity, another crow had come flying up the glen as if mocking her.

The antagonism that Gruilma experienced, however, was much the same as that which urged the crow to vent her spite on the injured goose. She too remembered an event of the previous evening when her mate was struck down in Glen Sligachan. It gave her a queer satisfaction to harry something that could no longer drive back at her. By so doing, it seemed that she was, in some vague way, avenging her mate's death.

Then, as Gruilma came gliding overhead, the crow became aware of the danger that threatened her, and to reach her nesting site way over against the flank of Glamaig, she essayed an escape into the wind. She rose clumsily, causing the wounded goose, who also feared an attack, to seek protection amongst those of his clan now spread out along the whole line of the slow-ebbing sea.

Before the goose had reached his objective, the crow was well up in the wind, beating her way with all haste for the shelter of the few rowan trees that grew aslant the cleft that was once a quarry and was now the home of many wild creatures.

Gruilma had, by now, taken a pitch directly above the fleeing bird. The wind currents which were proving such a formidable adversary for the crow helped to support the eagle who rode them with ease. As the wind blew a little stronger, more exacting than ever became the crow's battle to reach the rowan trees in the quarry. Fully aware of the great threat directly above her, she let out a broken "Krark-krark!"

It was as she cried out in her distress that Gruilma turned in the wind and, cutting a complete arc in the sky, swept down on her — a winged fury that gathered impetus as it hurtled earthward and brought instant death even before the first feathers went streaming away on that sea-going wind.

Having struck, Gruilma banked away, swooping upward from the falling body of her victim as if with disdain. She then went gliding on the race of the wind in the direction of the coarse grassland where she turned her attention to the rabbits who had suddenly appeared from their burrows.

When later she made off once again for the plateau where she had roosted the previous night, she passed like a ghostly shadow over the isolation of the glen, quiet now save for the bray of the wind in the rowan trees in that quarry where so many creatures dwelled secure from one such as she.

At last Gruilma settled herself on the grassy ledge that had long been the haunt of others of her kind, and as she turned about prior to sleeping, she saw, far down in the west, the star of the Falconidae.

Soon she slept, while slow went the twilight, twisting up the glen like a living thing nosing in and out of the mountains. By the time it was completely dark, the star of the Falconidae was no longer visible in the west. Where it had been had risen a fleet of cloud; and it was not long before both wind and rain came fretting at the mountains and the glens, and the lost night birds down by the river went crying out in the smore of the storm that had taken them unawares.

CHAPTER NINETEEN

NO ROAD RUNS BY

STILL CRYING THEY WERE WHEN THE STORM, EXHAUSTED by its own fury, died away, and dawn came, dim and bedraggled, over the eastern hills. A chill morning it was too, after the rain, with every indication that it would be a cold and louring day, for down against the flank of the mountain the sheep stood with tails to the wind, while near by, the race of the Sligachan River was little better than a tumbling, shrieking flow of tempestuous currents that set small boulders trembling in midstream, and caused tiny whirlpools to appear where once had been quiet backwaters where trout were wont to lie.

Up on the very summit of the mountains, trails of mist flew east with the wind, only to be followed by great wracks of vapor that resisted the higher streams of air and thus remained clinging to the peaks until nothing could be seen save the lower walls of rock visible only a little way above that grassy plateau where Gruilma slept late.

At last the eagle roused herself. Below she heard the thin treble of a lamb calling its mother, heard too the roar of the river and the shrill crying of curlews above the bogland at the foot of Marsco.

She then remembered Greeka, and without further hesitation, sailed off the plateau and made for the higher reaches of Loch Sligachan and the coarse grassland where, the previous night, she had successfully hunted rabbits.

None, however, could she see on this morning of mist and chill, driving rain. The whole of the grassland area was deserted, and the small rabbit paths were, for the most part, just tiny rivulets that drained into the higher reaches of the loch.

The density of the clouds had increased during the short turn Gruilma made over the rabbit warren, and the rain, now torrential, came sweeping in from the sea in looping whorls that went scudding across the stretch of moor to Sligachan and the wild, silent glen that lay between the mountains. Even as the eagle banked before sailing along the loch shore, she heard, close beside a burn, the startled pipe of a whaup, followed by the sharp complaint of an oyster catcher.

An instant later both whaup and oyster catcher were forgotten as, flying low along the whole of the shoreline. she found that all the geese had gone, the redshanks also. Only one still shape remained to attract her attention — a shape that neither moved nor protested as she swooped low over it.

It was the goose that had been injured. In the night, the great Spirit of the Feathered Tribe had taken compassion on it, and only the lifeless body now remained — a pitiful, drab thing, lapped by the slow-ebbing tide and of no use to anyone — not even to the eagle who was hungry and industriously searching the whole of the loch and the glens adjacent to it.

After a few seconds, Gruilma beat her way inland, making for the quarry where she took up a position on a nearby crag and waited for some prey to appear from amidst the rowan trees.

For a very long time she sat quietly upon the storm-swept crag, watching the tossing and dancing of the rowans in the squally bursts of wind. Slowly a pool gathered in a hollow directly at the foot of the crag. At first it was little more than a shimmer of water splintering each time the rain fell in it; then, quite soon, it spread out until it became a small lake on which frail green leaves eddied like boats in a storm-shapen loch.

All Gruilma did was to blink occasionally and once or twice to ruffle her feathers. For her, time did not exist.

The minutes sped by; the quarry might have been completely deserted. Nothing seemed ever to happen there save, as now, the tossing of the trees in the wind, and the deepening and widening of the pool which was now being fed by a small run of water from off the crag itself.

Yet Gruilma waited. Not for herself this watchfulness in the smore of the storm, but for Greeka who could no longer hunt for himself.

Suddenly she stiffened as she sat on her lofty perch. A faint sound had reached her ears. Then her patience was rewarded by the sudden darting forward of a plump pigeon, followed by his more timid mate.

The rowan tree, in which they had both been sheltering and hiding, had scarcely shaken the first of the rain from its leaves as they hastened away when Gruilma glided silently off the crag, and in a trice was upon them, striking first one bird and binding it in her talons, then the other before either had knowledge that it was death itself which swept down on them in the wind.

At the very moment of the kill, the eagle had turned, with the pigeons firmly clutched and held beneath her. She then climbed swiftly up the wind, and in the same number of heartbeats that it had taken her to make the dual attack, she was heading for the lodge and the barred enclosure where Greeka had been imprisoned.

Back in the quarry, the rowan trees were still tossed and tormented by the wind; the pool at the foot of the crag still deepened and spread. The water, however, was not quite so clear as it had been.

There was a hint of red in it now as if from blood.

Gruilma cut a wide arc above the mist-shrouded summit of Glamaig, and went swinging down toward the place where she hoped her mate to be. She gave a low call as she breasted the wind currents, and then keeled over as the enclosure and the lodge itself came into view.

Another call she gave as she flew direct for the huge cage, but no movement was there this time to greet her, no upward turning of a golden-brown head . . . nothing! Greeka was no longer there!

She let go her grip on the pigeons and then fluttered down. Her head turned from left to right in her perplexity. The sweep of the wind through the bars of the cage disturbed a couple of feathers that lay in the center of the enclosure. There were also the remains of the rabbit she had brought to Greeka the previous day.

She straightened herself a little, shifted her weight from one foot to the other. There was no need for her to listen intently, for there was nothing for her to hear.

Gruilma could not understand why her mate was not in the cage to greet her. That he was alive, she had not the slightest doubt. If the great darkness had come to him during the night, or even during the first gray glimmering of the dawn, he would be there now — unmoving, bedraggled perhaps, like the goose that lay on the shore of the loch.

As if to make sure that the cage was indeed deserted, she gave a queer call in her throat. Her head half turned, her eyes shone brightly as she tried to see into the small walled-off space in the far corner of the enclosure.

She was satisfied then that Greeka had gone, for no answer came to her cry — no sound answered at all save the wind and the rain, and a sudden fluttering movement from the two feathers that were lifted and tossed about as a particularly strong gust caught them up in invisible fingers.

Gruilma stood motionless, leaning against the wind as this realization welled up in her with each quickening beat of her heart. No undue effort of reasoning was necessary to tell her what she wished to know. The core of the problem was contained in the fact that Greeka had been alive when last she saw him in this grim place of bars. Because she had no direct knowledge of the power of man over the animal kingdom, the only mystery she could not solve was his absence, particularly since no avenue of escape was possible for one imprisoned. What she did know — and this it was that gave her such knowledge of life and death — was that Greeka was certainly not like the goose down there on the shore of the Sligachan loch.

Such being the case, he would, one day, come back to the haunts he knew.

Gruilma's reactions, therefore, were such that she spread her pinions. No further time did she waste on that deserted enclosure, of no further interest to her those two golden-brown feathers that still twisted and fluttered in the squally bursts of wind. She soared upward on a strong current of air, thrusting up a little as she encountered a contrary current that cut across the roof of the lodge.

Then high above the phantom galleons of the clouds she went — a lone bird whose mate had been spirited away. Higher still, she swung up out of the wrack of gray, clinging cloud into a clear blue sky where the sun shone brightly and where two buzzards sailed in widening circles, wailing all the time like kittens in distress.

No mate, however, was up there in the blue to join her. Greeka, the eagle from the Clach Glas corrie, who had brought her from the mountain wastes of Ross-shire, was not here in the sunshine beyond the wrack of storm-driven cloud. Yet — and she believed it as surely as she knew that day must give way to night — there would come a time when he would be traveling the air lanes of the sky with her again. She, like all of her clan, had mated for life, and would wait until the monarch of the Sligachan glen came sailing back over the eastern hills to end her hours of solitude.

Then down out of that sun-dappled blue she went, keeling over, and leaving the two buzzards still mewing to each other. Down once more she went into the gray drift of cloud and the rain that filled the burns to overflowing and caused the small lochans to spread across the glens until they resembled land-locked seas at the foot of the mist-draped mountains.

No more, for the time being at least, did she visit the eyrie above the Clach Glas corrie. For the present she remained on the grassy plateau on Sgurr nan Gillean from which she could stare across the glen in the direction of the white lodge and the Red Hills that rose beyond.

So began the long vigil which only the return of her mate could end!

CHAPTER TWENTY

A MONARCH IN EXILE

IN THE DEEP SILENCES OF THAT NIGHT WHEN GRUILMA
slept for the first time alone on the plateau, Greeka sat mop-
ing in the cage. The whit-owl called for the last time in the
byre and the lamps of the lodge went out one by one. For a
long while he sat in one corner of the cage, listening to the
distant sounds that came to his ears, suddenly ruffling his
feathers, when the stag he had saved from man belled out
as if in defiance.

Unseeing, he stared out into the darkness. Then it seemed
his ears heard no more the night sounds. The wind probed
at him with rain-moistened fingers — the same that had
plucked from the stalk up on the plateau that white blob of
cotton grass and sent it wandering like a wraith down the
glen.

He could not sleep. He sat, with his head sunk deep in
his neck feathers, not hearing the drumbeats of the wind up
on Glamaig, nor yet feeling the scud of rain through the bars
of the cage. Neither did he see the dawn come up — that
rampant, fiery dawn that blazed and spread over all the

eastern horizon and sent Gruilma off down the glen in search
of the rabbit she was to bring in to him.

Yet Gruilma he saw, even before she had planed down to
the roof of the enclosure with the rabbit held in her talons. It
was as though he knew the instant she came over the ridge
of Glamaig. Then he fought his last fight for freedom which
ended only when he had damaged still further his primaries,
and the old sheep dog, Greyboy, stared in at a no-longer struggling bird.

It was the damage the primary feathers had sustained that
caused the owner of the lodge — a Fellow of the Zoological
Society — to decide to send Greeka first to Glasgow Zoo for
treatment, from whence he was to be sent on to the Regent's
Park Zoo in London. The foot should heal, and the damaged
feathers be renewed after the bird's usual moult.

Thus, on that very night when the twilight went slowly
twisting up the glen like a living thing searching in and out
of the mountains, the eagle was suddenly placed in an
enormous hamper. By the time the wind and the rain were
fretting at the hills, and the lost night birds were crying
down the whole length of the Sligachan River, he was on his
way.

The next twenty-four hours passed slowly, and he knew
nothing of the journey he made, being confined all the time
in the hamper. In it were a rabbit and a can of fresh water.
Not that Greeka ate or drank. He was far too miserable and
frightened. This strange new place of captivity afforded

him even less space than the barred enclosure had done.

Then, curiously, like many another creature of the wild before him when made captive, the instinct to submit overwhelmed all other considerations. He lost the desire to struggle further, lost too a little of his fear. This was replaced by a strange indifference that recognized no new change in his circumstances or surroundings. From a fierce bird of prey, he became a passive creature that even permitted people to handle him when he eventually arrived at the Glasgow Zoo.

Again, after a while, he was packed into a hamper. This time, a long rail journey ended in another barred enclosure that looked out over an immense London park where crows nested in tall trees, and other small birds continually thrust up into a strange sky that possessed none of the characteristics of the sky he had known from birth. The clouds he saw were heavy and slow-moving; the blue he sometimes glimpsed had none of the clearness of that northern sky over the mountains he knew as home.

He was perplexed and downcast. He sensed that he was far, far from the land of his birth!

Slowly that first spring day of his captivity in a London Zoo passed, and night came earlier to the south than it did to the north. As the shadows dropped down over a city abustle with activity, and folk began to take their evening stroll across Regent's Park, in the Zoological Gardens, it became very quiet.

Greeka, up on the platform that was to be his roosting

place, had not touched the rabbit that had been thrown in to him for his evening meal. He was staring away to the north, his eyes watching the Pole Star rise, and the day depart toward those far Hebridean islands that were his home.

The evening shadows deepened, and over seven hundred miles away, on that green plateau on the eastern cliffs of Sgurr nan Gillean, his mate sat and waited. For her, no city lights were springing up to dim the stars, no roar of traffic to silence the voice of the burns. She was free, yet in her freedom, she sat and waited.

As day succeeded day, Greeka was subject to much attention. He soon became reconciled to seeing people standing outside his enclosure, taking little notice of the Harpy Eagle in the next cage who danced and flapped his wings.

For many long hours at a stretch, Greeka sat up on the platform, unmoving, listless, sometimes gazing out across the expanse of the park where children walked and played, and small birds darted from tree to tree. The eagle could not understand why it was no longer possible to spread his pinions and soar — why the mountains and glens had been replaced by this grim place of bars.

All the experiences brought about by his fight with Panzeed in Harta Corrie were still real in his diurnal mind. It was as though the part of him that retained visions was also the part that gave vent to a rising tide of anger when the lions roared at feeding time. More than any other sound, the roar of beasts brought out the fearless spirit that captivity sought to subdue — that, and the soft fall of rain.

Rain Greeka had known from birth. The scud of it before gusts of wind took him back to the desolate wastes of his homeland more than did anything else. It took him away from the sights and sounds in the Zoo. He often dreamed of it as he squatted on his perch, but its significance was momentarily lost on waking, for through the bars of his enclosure he saw it only as drops of moisture falling from an invisible sky. Then, having bridged in a split second of time the difference between dreaming and being awake, the sharp alertness that always followed gave him back his sense of remembrance. He saw in the drops the rain he had always known and loved, falling from clouds that trailed like smoke over somber mountains; he heard too the faint echo of it like something he remembered as pouring in a tumult of sparkling cataracts down the precipitous hills that had been his heritage.

In such moments, a wild fury would possess him. Those golden-brown pinions would attempt to open, the fierce eyes gleam. Just those things. No more! He had learned the futility of beating against prison bars. The rain might fall and the wind bid him follow, but he just watched and listened, his moment of fury spent and gone.

To him, in his captivity, the wind now called in vain. He knew he could not obey its entreaty. Thus, for most of the hours of every day, he sat and moped — a monarch in exile who still retained vivid impressions of the kingdom he had lost —

Greeka's circle of acquaintances grew as the first days of summer brought many new visitors to the Zoo. Some of the Fellows of the Zoological Society, to whom Greeka presented something of a problem, visited him regularly, and it was not long before the bird was able to recognize those who were most frequently in attendance.

These were the days when the flaming girdle of the sun brought no respite to those creatures whose daily lives were passed behind prison bars. Animals panted with the heat and showed less inclination to humor the whims of those strange beings who peered at them in their captivity.

Greeka was no different in this respect from the others. Although, as the long summer days went slowly by, he became accustomed to spending an inactive life in his huge cage, there were times when the sight of people roused in him a fierce fury.

He remained on his platform from which he could ignore the crowds below and stare away to the still, transparent sky of the northern horizon, seeing, as the summer progressed, the faint irregular quiver of heat waves and the far-off glint of steeples against the cloudless blue.

Somewhere — beyond that vista of steeples and towers — he sensed that the scene was altogether different. Somewhere, away in the extreme north, the sun was not so hot. There the light went beaming and quivering up and down the heights and haughs of the untilled land.

Of those who were regular visitors to the cage, the most important to Greeka was, of course, his keeper, who brought him the freshly killed rabbits that were his main diet. He spoke to him quietly, seeking to soothe the eagle when he was inclined to be nervous.

It was not long before the eagle learned that his day held two major events, his feeding times. They broke the monotony of the long hours, and always, after his evening meal, he repaired to his platform to watch the day dying in the west and the new night come up out of the east.

Always, when the first star had risen and the whole of the northern skyline was slowly wheeling into the darkness of the new night, Greeka dreamed of his lost mountain home. If every sense were alert it seemed there might, then, be a husky call in the wandering night breeze, the scent of bracken and heather, and the sharp, brittle murmuring of water breaking and foaming over boulders, maybe too, the deep belling of a stag high up on some mountain summit, or the keening of an otter at the head of a loch, mourning, as otters often do, the loss of a mate or a cub.

One of the most remarkable of his visions was not drawn from the conditioning views and impressions of his own life. It had belonged only to Groonah, his mother, yet it was one of the strongest of his dream impressions.

It happened on a night when the summer wind brought with it the black cloud of a gathering storm. Greeka, in his sleep, might have been back again in the glens, for the mountains were all about him, and hunters were out on the hills. A sound, clearly heard even in his sleep, brought to life the sight of a hind coming down off a scree slope, trailing a broken leg. She cried out as she moved, raised high her head to stare straight at the hunter who knelt near by. No hesitation was there in her walking. No fear now of man. Even when the hunter put the gun to his shoulder, straight toward him she came so that he could end her misery and bring her, with peace, to that dark loch at World's End where no more would she be hunted nor endure the agony of broken bones.

When Greeka awakened suddenly to what he thought was the shot, it was the roar of thunder he had in his ears, and the grim sight of lightning flaring away behind the massed mountains of the clouds.

Where many another dream was, more often than not, completely forgotten as soon as he awakened, this — the one that came to him through Groonah — remained for a long time a recurring event in his diurnal consciousness.

With it too was an association which, unlike the dream itself, was something once vitally connected with him. He remembered Rooloo whom he had saved from a stalker's shot — Rooloo standing beside that small, twisty burn in the narrow glen betwixt Marsco and Beinn Dearg while the last of the day stood suspended in the gap dividing the two mountains.

He never doubted but one day he would again be quartering the hills in the glen, and hear Rooloo belling on his solitary height while he and Gruilma watched the winding course of the burn. It was when this conviction was most strong in him that he regarded, with exceptional excitement, the early morning visit of his keeper. Already Greeka knew that the man possessed the keys that opened the gate to the wider freedom beyond. Mornings there were when he was actually on the floor of his cage waiting for the keeper to put in an appearance. The man himself thought the bird was becoming reconciled to being held captive.

Thus passed the early days of summer. Soon it was midsummer, then late summer. Then coming rapidly behind the drift and drive of a north to northwestern wind was the birken dance of paling sunshine and deepening shadow upon the mottled grassland of the park, while loud sang a blackbird from his lofty perch in the trees outside the Zoological Gardens, so loud indeed that Greeka, hearing him, often inclined his head to listen.

There was no injured foot now to stop him from leaping up and down on his platform, no damaged feathers to mar the magnificent spread of his pinions.

He was in full plumage, each feather firm-set to ride the stormy toss of the wind.

He would only compose himself to sleep when the evening had gone down in dun color behind the steeples and towers of the great city, and the sky smoldered sullenly where, an hour since, the sun had been. Even then, in his ears, echoed the blackbird's last song — "Cheeri-kee — cheeri-kee — "

It was so like the song another blackbird used to sing from a less secure perch on an old green thorn tree beside the burn on Bealach Mor.

CHAPTER TWENTY-ONE

THE STAG HIS LAIR,
THE ERNE HER NEST

GREEKA'S HOUR OF ESCAPE APPROACHED WITHOUT ANY UN-
toward event to herald its coming. His last night in captivity was no different from the many other nights he had
known save that the dark had come earlier by reason of the
cloud which had come out of the west. A wind sprang up
and the sky began to brighten with the dawn. The clouds
showed signs of breaking up, and Greeka, asleep on his platform, became aware of the fingers of the wind probing him
to complete wakefulness. As he stirred, he heard from across
the park, the quiet, almost inaudible, cheeping of a bird
newly roused like himself. The sound was repeated, and as
Greeka half turned his head to hear it more clearly, it ceased
as the small bird sank back once again to sleep, the hour
still being very early.

For Greeka, however, there was no return to slumber. He
was restless. The wind had a song for him that morning —
an old, old song that was the song of the islands of the north
which it would soon visit. It was a strong wind too, traveling
swiftly from out of the southeast and heading direct north,

leaving the quarter moon like a ship tossed on a stormy sea and soon to be wrecked upon the ragged reefs of the cloud masses already driven to the northern horizon to await its sinking.

Rapidly then, from the wild drifting of the moon, seemed to kindle the great fire of the dawn, rising up and glowing behind the edge of the world. The black garment of the night was slowly rolled back; the stars flickered and, like the lamps of far-distant croftings, went out one by one until only a few gleamed less brightly in the very van of the sunrise. The gray behind the black turned to gold until a strip of the palest yellow lay astride the towers and steeples of a city stirring to a new day.

Then, as Greeka knew it would, the blackbird of the night before started to juggle with its notes. Clear and loud they trilled out across the dewy park — "Cheeri-kee — cheeri-kee."

Greeka, listening, sensed that the world had, indeed, wakened for his conquering!

Louder sang the wind; hard and clear sang the blackbird, and all the while the new day grew in splendor, and the few clouds that remained — remnants of the more stormy galleons of the night — were little more than frail craft slipping out of a quiet harborage on a long voyage to the north in the wake of the sinking moon.

It was a long while before Greeka became aware of the keeper approaching. He saw the man coming from the di-

rection of the Bird House, and the eagle immediately be-
stirred himself, swooping suddenly from the platform on
to the floor of the cage where he sat waiting.

So many things were happening in that tense moment —
things that had no direct connection with Greeka himself,
but were yet closely allied to all creatures great and small.
Most of those trivial things were in the race of the wind, in
the song it sang.

Some of them were in the whirling of a leaf recently blown
from a tree that went fluttering across the path and below
the moving feet of Greeka's custodian. The wind, however,
had still an important part to play, inasmuch as it swept the
leaf from beneath the keeper's feet and sent it flying upward.
As the man looked up, his attention was caught and held
by the movement of a kestrel flying high above the park.
Palpitating with life and energy, the bird hung in the air
currents — well called the windhover.

The keeper was still interested in the kestrel when he
came to Greeka's cage and fumbled with the key that opened
the gate. Scarcely had the lock turned beneath his fingers
than he glanced up once again to see if the hawk was still
visible. The man nodded his head with satisfaction, and
thought, momentarily, how perfectly balanced the bird was
in the flow of the wind.

He then felt the gate swing inward beneath his hands.

Bending his head to enter the cage, he was about to cross
the threshold when, like a mottled brown flash, Greeka made

his sudden bid for freedom. It was decisive, and he was out through the swinging gate and across the path before the keeper was quite aware that he had gone.

Greeka fluttered wildly, even clumsily. It was clear he had yet to regain the strength that had been lost in captivity. He heard the keeper shout, and turned away from an obstacle in the shape of a post and a stretch of fencing directly ahead. In doing so, he found himself in line with a plot of grass.

He touched down for a moment, with his feet firm-pressed on the sward. Then the wind — his ally — came to him, and in a second he was rising — soaring higher and higher above the place where he had been held prisoner; higher still he went until he was beyond even the kestrel who had been a silent witness to his escape.

Even as the small hawk keeled over, Greeka, now in complete control of his pinions, swung around in the cold race of the wind, and hit the airlines of migration — those invisible trails which, year by year, are followed by those in search of the sun.

Greeka, however, was not facing the south. Due north he set his head. With a slow movement of his mighty wings, he set off toward the place where the quarter moon had already foundered on the cloud reefs.

Below him, carried on a fitful eddy of the wind, a few brown feathers twirled in the air — all that remained of the small sparrow the kestrel had seen as he keeled over.

Greeka was over open country in a matter of minutes. He had scarcely noticed the change in the scene below, so intent was he on reaching a safe height in the sky, and following the course of the wind.

Suddenly he saw the chalk escarpment of the Chiltern Hills on his left wing tip, and while from the height at which he was flying he could also see the many small villages that nestled within their outlying spurs, he wheeled slowly to investigate their possibilities for hunting. Running straight across the main ridge was a track which attracted Greeka's special attention, and in less than a dozen wingbeats, he was flying low over it in search of rabbits.

Thus for the first time in many decades did an eagle quarter the chalk hills of the south and stoop over copses that fringed the ancient Icknield Way and the Roman Stane Street.

It was cool, that morning of Greeka's brief sojourn along the ridge of the Chilterns, and hunting was much to his liking.

About noon, however, his hunting came to an abrupt end. Men were beating their way up the ancient ridgeway, all searching for the golden eagle that had escaped from the London Zoo.

Greeka took off on a favorable turn of wind, and was away over the ridge and out of sight without being glimpsed by those who sought him. He could now sense danger in every movement he saw, and as a safeguard, he spiraled up and up until he was lost in a high ceiling of cloud vapor.

The wind at this altitude was sharp and moving steadily, and still was it traveling northward. As a result, Greeka went with it, and was soon over the dales of Derbyshire which were more to his liking, and showed less signs of habitation than the Chilterns.

He found a lofty crag upon which to perch — a crag that was close to a swiftly flowing stream. It was of limestone formation, but possessed an isolation that Greeka favored. Moreover, it was one of a series of precipices contained in a wide sweep of hills that terminated in what was known locally as The Peak — a height of some two thousand feet. Across the wide valley through which flowed the stream, Greeka could discern the almost straight course of a canal that connected one of the larger towns with another on the distant Yorkshire border.

The whole area was densely wooded, and beyond the curve of the hills, that afforded temporary sanctuary to the eagle, was a viaduct built up on five arches. A thin spiral of smoke marked the passage of a train that was traveling over it on its long journey to the north.

In watching the smoke trail of the express, Greeka finally found himself surveying a long, irregular line of hills in the extreme northwest — hills that rose tier upon tier to a much higher elevation than these which now afforded him protection.

He was attracted to them, that serrated outline reminding him somewhat of the mountains of his homeland. Even as he gazed at them, there grew in him the knowledge that when another day came to this strange land he must be away and visit them.

Little did he know that those far-off hills on the northwestern horizon were the mountains of the Lake District, and indeed, for him, the stepping stones to the greater mountains that lay across the Scots border. For the time being, however, he realized the urgent need for rest, and looked out over the wide vale below to ensure that it was good hunting country, and the crag a good and safe nesting site.

He had no means of knowing that for all these precautions, his stay on the crag was for just this one night, that on the morrow, those mountains of the northwest would bring him such vivid memories of his homeland that he must needs journey on.

Then, because the day was drawing to a close and he must eat before night came, he went quartering the dale to the annoyance of some crows who nested in a copse adjacent to the river. As he beat his way slowly up the valley, they attempted to mob him, but like all of his kind, he ignored them and went about his hunting in an industrious manner. Close beside the river, and under the lee of a frowning cliff, he caught two rabbits, one of which he ate on the spot, carrying the other in his once injured foot back to his nesting site on the crag overlooking the dale.

At last, contentedly, he rested, happy in his new-found freedom, and stared down across the wide dale while the crows, who less than an hour since had tried to mob him, bickered amongst themselves in the copse beyond the turbulent stream.

The evening grew in strength over The Peak and traveled in heavy shadow over the dales and up the silent hill slopes. For more than a thousand, thousand years had the night come thus to this dale and the ridge of hills that stretched away northward. For more than a thousand, thousand years had birds sat as Greeka now was sitting, while the crows, who had inhabited the dale long before the first eagle came, and remained the black guardians of the valley from the very hour when the last eagle was banished to the far-off mountains of the north, bickered as now they were bickering, as indeed they had bickered from the very dawn of time.

Quietly drained the light from the sky, and with the darkness, the last crow ceased his muttering and slept with head under wing.

Toward the hour of midnight, the quarter moon burst from behind a bank of cloud, and sudden light leaped up the whole width of the dale. It was then that a night bird whistled out sweet and shrill, and Greeka, stirring himself, thought he was back on Clach Glas, and hearing the curlews calling down by the Sligachen River.

CHAPTER TWENTY-TWO

THE RETURN TO THE GLEN AND THE HOLLOW HILLS

THE DAWN CAME UP WITH A RACE OF CLOUD, THE WIND blowing wet and chill. Here and there the tracery of cloud shapes passed and repassed over the dale and the distant mountains of the northwest. An early lark sang clear and sweet above the stream. One or two willows, close beside the stream, stood shivering and complaining when the wind struck at them with its lash that was, after all, but a fore-taste of what was to come when September was a memory and the scud of snow and sleet came from off the hills of the north.

Greeka was awake early, and after making a meal off the rabbit he had brought in the previous evening, sat for a long while preening his breast feathers, while the lark continued to sing, and one by one the crows, in the copse across the river, left their nests and set off raucously about their business.

At last Greeka disgorged some of the pellets of fur and bone necessary to aid his digestion, and prepared to set off a-journeying. By now the sun was well up, and the scurry of cloud shapes over the higher regions of the hills told of the swift passage of the high-swinging wind.

As the eagle left the crag and floated out over the dale, a couple of crows thrust up at him. Ignoring them, he keeled over, and then encountering the race of the air currents, set his course northwest.

Traveling at a high altitude, he made unerringly for his objective, aided by the strong flow of the wind which was steadily veering from east to north-northwest. Keeping in line with the mainly agricultural strip of country between High Peak in the dales of Derbyshire and Bottom Head Fell in the northern Pennines, he soon approached the mountainous region of the lakes.

He found himself thrilling in every feather to each turn of the wind; the haze of the industrial areas way off on his left wing tip did not worry him. Ahead he could see clearly enough the serrated shapes of the mountains he was determined to reach, and set at their feet, huge lakes like the lochs he remembered so well in his native country.

A little before high noon, sunglow lay upon the fells that rose up ahead, and the bracken, already bronzed by the early fall, and fading, seemed ablaze with light as Greeka turned and began to plane earthward. Shadow-threaded in the sun, the fern patterns were darkling at the roots, and the eagle passed low, seeking out any unsuspecting creature that might be hidden there in the gloom.

He showed no sign of weariness although he had journeyed

more than a hundred miles since leaving the roosting crag
in the dales of Derbyshire. Backward and forward he went,
passing over and over again the wilderness of bracken and
making sudden swoops whenever something of interest attracted his attention.

A low cloud, trailing over the peak of Red Pike, broke in
a thin drift of rain before passing over Bleaberry Tarn and the
lake of Buttermere and Dale Head.

Greeka was feasting off a young rabbit when the cloud
broke up over Red Pike. There was a stillness and complete
silence in the bracken where he squatted eating, and then
came the swift patter of the rain, so soon to depart as the
cloud, now little more than a thin veil of mist, drifted away,
taking the rain with it.

All that afternoon, Greeka quartered the high ridge of
mountain, starting with High Crag in the south, and ter-
minating in Red Pike in the north. On one side of the ridge
were the lakes of Buttermere and Crummock Water — both
in the east, and in the west, Ennerdale Water, while in the
extreme north, the very small lake of Lowes Water. Beyond
the lakes, and seeming to go on and on, were the scarred
shapes of mountains, with dark little tarns lying in their
midst, and the moors and near foothills dark-shadowed by
the racing clouds above.

Greeka loved it all. He turned and turned in tireless
flight, his recent period of imprisonment completely forgotten. Time and time again did he thrust up into the very

spin of the wind as excitement gripped him and urged him to perform feats of prowess high above the mountain peaks.

All that afternoon — long in sunshine for that time of year — the heatherland shimmered in the autumnal haze, and Greeka, more beautiful than he had ever been before in his new plumage, with his auburn head rising and falling as his wings swept the air, quartered unceasingly the purple hills and pencil-darkened hollows where here and there a small eye of water winked up at the sun.

Then, as the sun started to go swiftly down in the west, Greeka went sailing off the summit of Grassmoor, south of Brackenthwaite Fell, his shadow racing behind him. He spiraled rapidly as he approached Crummock Water, not noticing that another bird was hovering above the heights of Red Pike. It was smaller by far than any eagle, and the wings were long and sickle-shaped so that it had the appearance of a silver cross.

It was Kee-nee, the peregrine falcon!

As Greeka breasted the air streams over Crummock Water, a wild duck skimmed the surface of the lake, and rising suddenly, attempted to make for Bleaberry Tarn.

In a trice the eagle swung around and went into a stoop. So too did Kee-nee. The peregrine was hurtling down at a speed that matched the eagle's, and even before Greeka could reach the now agitated fowl who had sensed danger, Greeka's contestant had dived past him, struck, and bound the stricken duck in a remorseless grip, and then soared upward, rising almost under the eagle's very tail feathers.

Greeka, resentful at what had happened, made a sharp turn. He remembered when Vigur, the sea eagle, had struck down a mallard over Loch Airnort, and was this time aware of anger at having been bested by a bird so much smaller than the sea eagle.

He thrust up at the peregrine. Kee-nee was as good a hunter as the sea eagle had been, equally swift on the wing. He had not the slightest intention of giving up what he considered his by right of claw. The very instant Greeka came up toward him, he made a twist out of reach, and then, with a hiss of his steely-blue feathers, shot past Greeka in the stupendous dive that he made. He streaked down the entire depth of the sky, gathering speed as he went, and yet not relinquishing his grip on the duck.

It was not a happy situation for the eagle who turned as the falcon went past him, and then continued to wheel as Kee-nee went swiftly earthward. Then, as Greeka was completing the second turn he had made, Kee-nee, more than a thousand feet below, pulled out of the dive, and with perfect grace, went gliding over Crummock Water to take refuge in the small copse on its western bank.

In no circumstances would Greeka have eaten prey not of his own killing. He accepted his defeat with a return of his usual good humor, now that the peregrine was not visible to remind him of the incident. He therefore went spiraling down toward the ridge of Red Pike where he decided to find a roosting place for the night.

He found a suitable gully on the eastern cliff of the mountain which looked down upon Bleaberry Tarn and the small stream known as Sour Milk Gill, so named because it was little more than a streak of white foam descending from the tarn itself. South of the gill was an expanse of wood which, as the evening advanced, caught and held the last of the sunlight and thus shadowed the rapidly darkling water of Buttermere.

There were no crows in the valley to disturb him; no lark to sing. It was quieter by far than the dale in which he had roosted the previous evening, and as Greeka sank into sleep, he knew the quietness to be that same quietness which he had experienced on Bealach Mor.

He gurgled contentedly in his throat, knowing that already he was far from the place that had held him captive, and that the home of his birth was waiting beyond.

His last recollection was the sight of the Pole Star rising, and Altair, the Star of the Falconidae, sinking in the northwest where the last of the day was fading.

No further sign did he need to tell him the direction he should go when another day dawned. The pathway to the isles was already sign-pointed for him to follow.

Greeka was not for lingering or sleeping late now. No sooner had the first wood pigeon called to his mate down in the copse than he was wide awake, and before another of the feathered tribe stirred, he was quartering the fell lands between Sour Milk Gill and Scale Beck. Then, having successfully trapped his first rabbit, he remained only long enough on the saddle of Red Pike to digest it, and was off in the wake of the Pole Star which had gone down in the northern sky two good hours before.

His flight that day took him over the entire district of the lakes, and toward evening, he crossed from England into Scotland. Since the border country with its rolling Cheviot Hills held little attraction for him after the mountains, he journeyed into the very path of the westering sun, until he came at last to a district of loch and hill that was heavily timbered. The hills were not the rugged hills of the north, but they were none the less familiar in outline, and hunting in the narrow straths was good.

That evening, as the last of the day died in the west, and the moon came up on the crest of a storm cloud, Greeka discovered in the Forest of Glen Trool, Benyellary — the Hill of the Eagle. Thus, after many decades, an eagle came to rest briefly in this forestland of the south from which his race had been driven by man.

Almost as if he were familiar with the district, Greeka sailed down to rest on the old eyrie. As night came up out of the east, he stared over the expanse of Merrick Mountain to Loch Enoch, set high up in a fold of the mountain, the Loch of Ice as it was once called in the days when the eagle was no stranger to the Forest of Glen Trool.

Tired of watching the invasion of darkness upon this land of hill and loch, he fell asleep just as the Loch of Ice dwindled and vanished, and from way over on Dungeon Hill a peewit called.

During the night, the moon foundered in the cloud masses that gathered above the glen of the Black Water of Dee; the wind rose, and in the early hours Greeka was aware of the misty drift of rain and the voice of a heron calling up from beyond the loch where the ground fell steeply from the Cairn to Loch Arron.

It was morning and Greeka woke to a plaintive sound. A wild thrill went through him. He shook himself and cried out with excitement. At last! At last! The old familiar scenes were growing before his eyes — mist and misshapen hills — hills that held the lochs in their grip; and in the forestlands, the surging of the wind in the larches.

Greeka left the eyrie and thrust up into the wind. Without a single thought of food, he flew first into the spate of the wind, then with it; all because he had heard a buzzard's cry. It reminded him of when he had brought Gruilma from the fastnesses of Beinn Eighe to Clach Glas while another buzzard had wailed over the solitudes of Loch Clair, and the music of the larches in Coulin Forest had been no less stirring than the music he heard now in the forestlands of the low foothills.

In such a manner then did Greeka, Eagle of the Hebrides, depart from the Galloway low country and with the wind,

breasted the Glencap hill to come at last to the higher hills
of Argyll. There, above the fingerlike shape of Loch Long,
he turned and wheeled with delight, recognizing in the serrated shape of Ben Arthur the formation of hills that led the
way to Inverness-shire and the far western islands of the
Hebrides.

Two days later, on the Isle of Skye the day, which had
broken in misty rain, continued gray, with here and there in-
termittent gleams of sunlight sweeping down through the
rifts in the widespread blanket of cloud. In such moments,
the beams of sunlight poured down upon the mountains and
moors like gold dust scattered from heaven itself. For a brief
instant, the lochs and the sea shone like polished mirrors
held in the grip of narrow horizons, the small tarns and
lochans like the eyes of the green moorland smiling up at
the face of eternity.

It was an incongruous world — that world of steaming
mountain and sun-swept loch that was confined within the
limits of the winged Isle of Skye.

On this autumn day, no scene bore the same resemblance
for more than a moment at the most. The entire island was
made up of change — sunlight and somber gloom — mist-
riven mountains engirdled with sudden splashes of color as
the beams of sunlight touched for a moment the green,
heather-clad moors before departing to more distant heights
that surveyed the world beyond the clouds.

Perhaps no place contained more atmospheric change than did Glen Sligachan when high noon had gone and the slow passing hours fell toward the edge of the day. Brief spells of rain brought a sparkle to the burns and a many-chorused symphony from the falls. Above them, the mountain peaks trailed banners of broken mist, the quivering sunlight softening at rare intervals the hills' rugged contours.

To the eagle, who soared over the summit of the Pinnacle Ridge of Sgurr nan Gillean, and alighted on the small grassy plateau where so many of her kind had nested in a bygone age, the glen was much as it had always been. Ever since her mate had been taken from her, Gruilma had never known it to be any different.

As she settled herself to renew the vigil, now become a habit in the months from spring into summer and summer into these first weeks of the fall, she heard, high up on Beinn Dearg, the sonorous call of a stag. The Hunting Winds were again loose on the hills, and Rooloo was belling his defiance.

The September day, despite the low-lying clouds, was long adying. Far down the glen, rounding wearily the flank of Ruadh Stac, plodded two climbers making for the Sligachan Hotel. Their voices carried in the breeze, and Gruilma glanced in their direction before resuming her solitary brooding.

Up on Beinn Dearg, the stag belled once more. It seemed as if he knew there were no stalkers on the hills that late afternoon. A drift of rain, with mist breaking over the ridge, muffled his voice. Only the sound of a sudden shout from the two climbers disturbed Gruilma.

Somewhat nervously, Gruilma turned on her nesting site and sat facing in their direction; she saw that they had paused and were staring upward. She became tense with excitement. She knew not what to expect, but the wind was full of friendly utterances. It did not speak of danger.

The two climbers quite suddenly resumed their steady plodding up the glen, once or twice glancing back at Ruadh Stac. Gruilma watched them.

Way over by the mountain of the Red Pile, the burn that flowed around the northern flank was in full spate. It swept over the boulders in a tossing crescendo of sound, causing some of the larger rocks in midstream to vibrate as the currents crashed ceaselessly against them. A skein of mist was drifting over the summit, torn from the many pennants fluttering over Clach Glas. Another scud of rain came sweeping up the glen. From beyond Marsco, the stag belled once again.

Then out of the mist came the shape of an eagle — the same bird that had attracted the attention of the two climbers. It was Greeka, returned at last to his native mountain! With the wind and the rain buffeting him, he planed down toward the glen, following the course of the burn. Then, at a point where the burn intersected the glen before flowing on to the Sligachan River, Greeka made a sharp turn, and came to rest on one of the rocks in midstream.

In the very second of his alighting, the rain passed over, and a clean, fresh wind blew cold from off the mountains.

Greeka stood poised for an instant, his talons gripping the rock, his head turning from left to right. No memory had he then of the long journey he had made to reach this place, no lasting impression of the vast chain of mountains he had followed to reach this hinterland of the islands. He only knew that he was home at last.

Then he spread once again his vast pinions, concentrating his might upon the gray sky waiting to receive him. As the surge of water broke against the base of the rock and was gone in a spumy torrent of sound, the eagle lifted himself, swung away in a wide arc, rose a little, then banked, coming back to rest once again upon the rock.

His talons gripped for a second time the smooth surface of the rock, his pinions opening slowly.

Before he took again to the air, a curlew whistled from down by the Sligachan River, and with it came another sound from off across the glen — the voice of an eagle!

The cry had scarcely died away when the black shape of Gruilma came hurtling over the glen and the two small lochans strung together like discs of ebony. Greeka rose in one magnificent sweep to meet her — rose higher and yet higher — his pinions tilted to catch the flow of the wind — his primaries clear-cut like scimitars against the sky.

The two birds met in mid-air, encircled each other, and

cried out in excitement before soaring higher still, thrusting up and up in easy, joyous flight.

A few seconds later, they dived through the strands of mist torn from the fluttering pennants on Clach Glas, and breaking the stoop just above the summit of Ruadh Stac, made direct for their old eyrie on the Blaven-Clach Glas ridge.

The curlew ceased to call. All was silent save for the symphony of the burn and the soft cry of the wind. Austere in their aloofness, the mountains steamed with mist while, through a gap in the clouds, the bronze shield of the sun went down slowly into the sea.

Here ends the story of Greeka, Eagle of the Hebrides, begun one spring at Carbost, on the Isle of Skye, and completed two years later at Torridon, Ross-shire, in the north-western Highlands of Scotland.